Emily B. Lehnert

All About Men

ALL ABOUT
men

Joseph H. Peck, M.D.

Drawings by Larry Reynolds

PRENTICE-HALL, INC.
Englewood Cliffs, N. J.

Library of Congress Catalog Card Number 58-8627

PRINTED IN THE UNITED STATES OF AMERICA

02228

First printing ——— *March, 1958*

Second printing ——— *May, 1958*

DEDICATED TO

the poor wretch awaiting his turn in a doctor's office and trying to dream up explanations for his troubles which would reflect upon his Creator instead of on his own foolishness;

and with thanks to

Monroe Stearns and Sally Johnson for their kind treatment of the author during the gestation of this little book.

Contents

PART I

From Pram to Hot Rod

PREFACE xiii

1. WHAT IN HEAVEN IS THIS? 3
2. THE WAR OF THE SEXES BEGINS 9
3. THE CHILD'S SIDE, YOUR SIDE, AND THE BACKSIDE . . 14
4. ARE YOUR GENES SHOWING? 24
5. "I ZINK MAYBE I DON'T KNOW" 32
6. OF MICE AND WOMEN 40

PART II

From Halter to Altar

7. PURSUE LEARNING, DON'T LEARN PURSUING . . 51
8. GO SLOW WHEN YOU A-WOOING GO 63
9. OH, WHAT WILL THE HARVEST BE? 71
10. SEQUEL TO THAT WEDDING TRIP 78

PART III
From Time Clock to Ticker Tape

11. Fictitious domination of the male 87
12. A pregnant wife has a whim of iron 95
13. It's cheaper to move than to pay rent . . . 107
14. Your children are not your children . . . 114

PART IV
From Old Age of Youth to Youth of Old Age

15. Plenty of room at the top 123
16. Be moderate . . . but don't miss anything . . 136
17. A pig bought on credit grunts all year . . 144
18. Wives are like old shoes 149

PART V
The Youth of Old Age

19. At full of tide 159
20. The lengthening shadow of the boy . . . 166
21. Killing time is suicide 171
22. Check your motor and fuel supply . . . 182
23. Whither thou goest, make her go . . . 188
24. Bringing down father 197

PART VI
The Time for Adventure

25. It's never too late to begin 207
26. Go native and save money 218
27. Friends that don't gossip 232
28. Hints for fruititarians and others . . . 236

PART VII
Twilight Years: Seventy-Five Plus

29. You're only old once 251
30. Post mortem thoughts 256

Preface

In this book I chronicle the life of the average man as I know him after long years of study of the subject. While you watch him as he makes his entrances and exits and plays his many roles in the consultation room of a country doctor, I hope you will recognize yourself enough to learn how to avoid some of the mistakes that generations of men before you have made. Many of my old friends may try to identify themselves with this average man, but they are not so identified in my mind. When in doubt, I called up the life I know best and tried to remember what the Peck kid did at various ages; and even at that, Peck is so blended with others who came after him that I'm not too sure of his identity.

The male child is born sightless, toothless, and with sore genital organs, and all he can to do to express his displeasure is yell and kick. Seventy-five years later we find him in the same fix, *sans* eyes, teeth, and prostate gland, once again unhappy about his situation.

Between this alpha and omega of man's existence there are

many summits to climb and plenty of rock slides and pitfalls, along with side trips and detours, to hinder the ascent. This book deals with some of the precipices and mud holes that caused the author and his contemporaries much grief and anguish.

All men are equal in a physician's office. Remove the big shot's fancy clothes and drape him in an examining gown and he is just another pot-bellied or thin-shanked old wreck quite similar to the skid row bum who has just had a bath and shave. I hope that after seventy-two years of living, many of them spent in the ringside seat of a doctor's office, I am able to give advice which may help future wayfarers bargain a bit more favorably with fate and circumstance; but my counsel is offered in humility.

This is not a how-to-do-it, uplift book by a pious do-gooder, nor is it a book for ambitious men or crackpot hypochondriacs. It's a book for ordinary men who are trying to feed their families, rear their kids properly, pay taxes, and keep a few steps ahead of the sheriff. Some other self-styled oracle can tell you how to live to be a hundred, but cock an ear if he begins by saying, "First, give up everything you enjoy"; for most of us imperfect humans are in the same boat as the late Alexander Woollcott, who said: "Everything I like is either illegal, immoral or fattening."

They say that after a few years of marriage, a man can look right at a woman without seeing her, and a woman can see right through a man without looking at him. Now, although even the best doctors are far less clairvoyant than the average woman, I'll stick out my neck far enough to say that a family or country doctor such as I was does learn a lot about Homo sap. I was the father confessor for Mormon, Catholic, Protestant, and other families, and a medicine man for a tribe of Gosiute Indians; and from my varied experiences I got considerable knowledge about what makes a man tick. A family

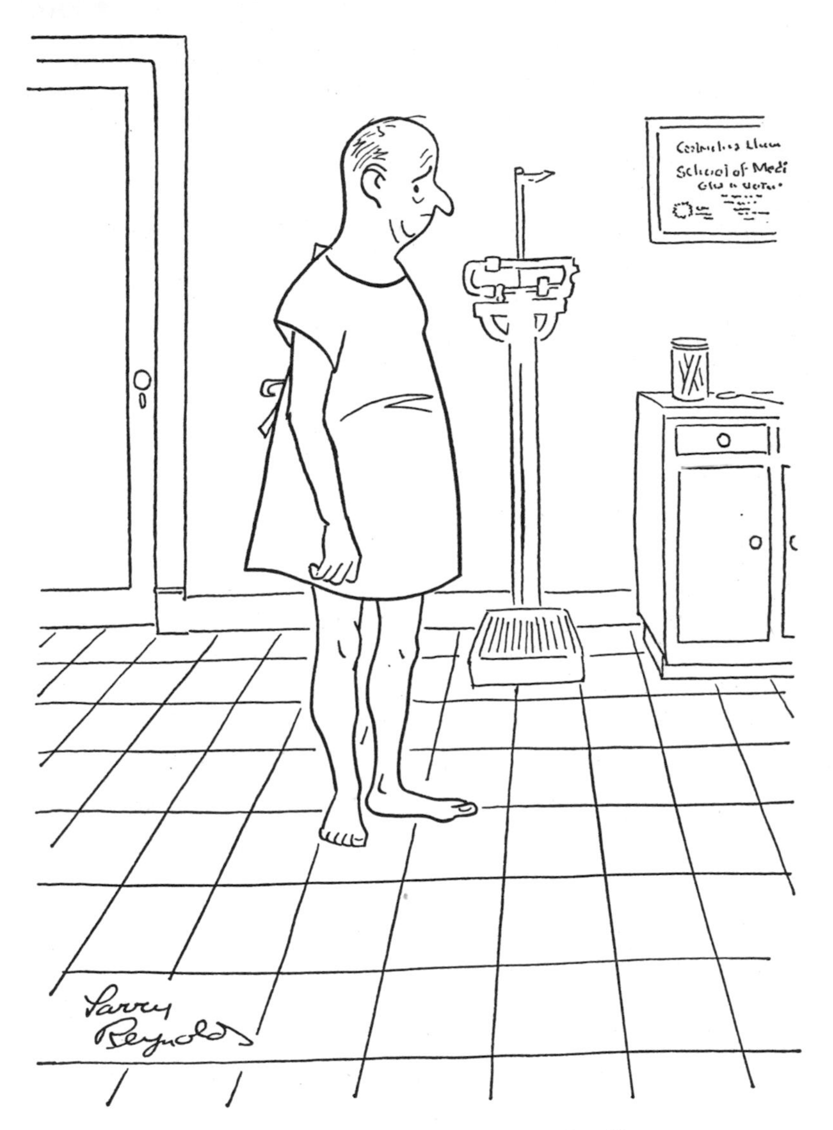

All men are equal in a physician's office.

doctor learns a great deal about the relationship between Mom and Pop and their paramours or concubines, along with the relationship between parents and their progeny—especially those born in wedlock.

It is a well known fact that graduates of medical schools are divided into three groups. The top third become professors, the middle group make the best doctors, and the lowest third make the most money. I think I belong to a fourth group—the one that has the most fun and satisfaction.

I have acted the part of a preacher in my time, but my pulpit was a flat-topped desk and individual sinners sat across from me, unable to dodge the issue by thinking that I was directing my remarks to some other wrong-doer in the congregation. I could sit down while expounding my sermons, and, unlike men of the cloth, was in no way restricted in my vocabulary when strong words were needed.

Now I am compounding the felony by writing a book. Well, the Lord should show compassion to sinners who have lived beyond their allotted span. It is His fault that we are still around and able to transgress. My aim is primarily to show you the side of man exposed in the doctor's consultation room and some of the asinine antics common to the human family. My patients varied greatly. One was a portly old church dignitary who claimed that he sprained his tail-bone while sitting in church through a long-winded sermon, but I must say that he was an exception, and he wasn't half so interesting as some of the gaycatting husbands and perplexed brides whose aches and pains were not acquired while sitting in a church pew. Many of them poured their problems into my ear.

Incidentally, I have never read the Kinsey report on the sex behavior of the male, and I sometimes wonder whether the late Dr. Kinsey read what he had written. I am convinced that the material was not gathered from average men, who would have been more likely to take a swing at the interrogator than describe their intimate sex life in a serious manner. The average guy shies away from discussing his sex life, but a family doctor, forced as he is to assume the role of father confessor in a small community, cannot help learning all about the billygoat complexes of men.

Being a physician—and there are no greater egotists—I have found fault with the way our Creator managed things pertaining to the reproduction of mankind, and I have thought of a number of changes I would have initiated had I been consulted in the matter. And being a doctor rather than a romanticist, I feel compelled to scrape the camouflage from the personality of my subject as I strip the clothes from his body, thus exposing some of his foibles as well as his good points.

The physician is fortunate in some respects. He is dedicated to the task of abolishing bad habits in others while he continues to enjoy these same habits.

But his ultimate goal is to return his patients to good health. Once this is done, they often prefer to forget the time of suffering and all things therewith connected. This includes paying the doctor's bill. One exception, however, is delivering a baby—a constant reminder of the doctor's services. Although the doc cannot conveniently repossess the merchandise, the parents, feeling a certain loyalty toward him, are more likely to pay for this service than for any other in any branch of the medical profession.

During thirty years of general practice I delivered more than two thousand live babies. I delivered one in a sheep wagon, others in box cars and tents, and one on a mountain peak. Since home deliveries were the custom, and telephones were scarce out on the Utah desert, I spent many idle hours awaiting the stork's arrival, and I naturally devoted some of them to thinking about the "sweet mystery of life."

I am not homesick for my old work, although I retired twelve years ago at the age of sixty to the Sierra Nevada foothills of northern California. This book will explain why. I enjoyed my life as a doctor, even if it sometimes meant traveling twenty-five miles on horseback through a couple of feet of snow to get to a patient. I made calls when it was twenty below zero and when the temperature rose to a hundred and ten degrees. During all the lonely vigils I had plenty of time for reflection, as I did while the stork's wings were flapping; and since settling down on my little farm, I have even more time for this lost art.

Years ago I attended a joint convention in Cleveland where the Associations of Industrial Surgeons and Industrial Engineers were gathered to discuss problems common to both groups.

By mistake, I wandered into a meeting of the engineers one morning, and because of the somewhat related fields, decided to remain and find out, if possible, just what they thought of us doctors.

I listened attentively to a speaker for an hour, but never a word got past my eardrums. He was using our common language, but just when I thought I had something to cling to, the speaker would turn to the blackboard and fill it with equations which bore little resemblance to the algebra of my student days.

I remarked as much after the meeting to the man sitting beside me.

"Now you know how the rest of us feel when we try to understand physicians," he said.

Right then I pledged myself never to let a patient leave my office until I had discussed his troubles in language a child could understand, using illustrations wherever possible. To get an idea over to a blast furnace worker, for example, I explained his pathological anatomy and physiology by comparing his poorly functioning heart valves to the pump of a cistern. He understood at once, because he had a first-hand knowledge of the extra effort required to obtain water when the pump was on the fritz. I'll use the same technique on you lucky readers.

That is, there will be no medical claptrap or mumbo-jumbo in this book. And because I am writing for lazy readers who hate dictionaries as much as I do, I will use more metaphors and analogies than are considered good practice in literary circles. This book will read the way I talk, and if the editors don't like it, they know what they can do.

JOSEPH H. PECK

All About Men

PART ONE

From Pram to Hot Rod

Youth is a wonderful thing; it's a crime to waste it on young people.

GEORGE BERNARD SHAW

1

What in heaven is this?

Between the first squall of babyhood and the dignity of adulthood is a delightful, ornery creature called a boy.

Boys come in assorted sizes, shapes, dispositions, and ability to get into trouble.

From birth to the age of eighteen, a male child needs parents who started training him from the moment he was born.

Junior needs a father of whom he can say, "That's my Pop." He needs a father whose eyes glisten just a little when, after a tough day at the office, he comes home and a tiny bundle of energy rushes toward him and says, "Hi, Dad."

Well, Dad, long before your son's keel was laid his troubles began, so don't blame him for crying the moment he is launched.

I have wasted lots of time trying to imagine just what went on in the celestial drafting rooms when these boy models were designed.

Since there is a similarity in construction to lower animals, we may assume that it was an assembly-line job, like a car advertised under a new name but made up of parts of former models.

The first unit to come off the assembly line was a fellow named Adam, and it wasn't too long before the stresses and strains of earthly hazards began to show the weak spots in his design. His head was too big for his chassis, and his shoulders were too broad; his hair, which added nothing to his beauty, was too sparse to keep him warm. His thatch was subject to quick obsolescence, and his whiskers would have looked good on the god Pan if only there had been a goat body to add grace to the production. His finished body, as bumpy looking as the original Studebaker wagon, was adorned with a couple of nipples which in no way could be regarded as ornamental or useful.

It was not fully understood just what sort of animal the celestial draftsmen intended him to be—whether fish, fowl or beast—so gills were put in his neck and then, when it was discovered that the muscle that should close his nostrils when under water was missing, the skin was drawn over them and only the tonsils were left hanging around to cause trouble. Sometimes this makeshift didn't work, so we find bothersome cysts marring the beauty of human necks—swan-like in youth, chicken-like in old age.

Two minor draftsmen must have met at the water cooler in heaven.

"I wish they would make up their minds in the front office just what this thing is going to eat," one angel said. "How in heaven am I going to draw a plan for something that may turn out to be a flesh-eater only, or a creature that grazes exclusively on grass, or a bird that lives on seeds? The boys in the back shop want him fixed up some way so he can do all three. They want this animal to be both carnivorous and herbivorous."

Second angel: "I'm supposed to attach the organs you design to the frame, yet I don't know whether he will fly, crawl, walk on all fours, or, as rumor has it, try the ridiculous stunt of balancing himself on his rear two feet."

So they installed his digestive organs with lax ligaments which, once he began to wear down a bit, allowed the whole mess to drop into the lower abdomen and make him look as if he were about to give birth to a litter of tomcats.

There was something left over after the small intestine was in place. Instead of removing it, they wadded it up and shoved it down into the lower right corner of his abdomen where it would not be noticed, never dreaming that freak offshoots of this queer animal would evolve into knife-happy surgeons who would transform this useless appendix into a gold mine.

The sex department should have made up their minds as to whether he was going to be a rooster and carry his sex glands in his back, or a mammal and leave them waving in the breeze.

Evidently this wasn't settled until the last minute, when they shoved them down through the abdominal wall, leaving a hole through which countless hernias could travel. The genital organs left dangling were not even leveled up, one hanging about an inch below its partner. The animal already looked a mess, so why bother about streamlining this item?

When the plumbing shop yelled because no outlet for bladder wastes was provided, it was told to latch onto the line the sex crew had installed for transmission of semen. It was concluded that one external organ would get the creature into enough trouble. If he had two, he would have no time to think about anything else.

When this compromise was made, and they finished covering his most important appendage, a segment of skin was left over. Instead of disposing of it right then, they gave it a twist and left it there for the obstetrician to snip off soon after his arrival in this vale of tears, an insult which would forever make him shy about his sex organ and most unhappy at the beginning of his journey.

The celestial draftsmen were right about the trouble this little appendage would cause. Any attachment required to function in two separate ways is subject to breakdowns in both respects, and a breakdown of one function prevents the other from performing its prescribed duties.

The model could have been improved in other ways. An extra stomach or two would have helped, for then, like a cow, man could have swallowed his food without chewing it (as he would often do anyhow) and ruminate at leisure. Better springs should have been installed in his feet, and those silly toe nails either should have been discarded or made strong enough to enable him to scratch for something useful, such as fish bait.

The chief designer, somewhat disgusted with this botched-up job, ordered a second model constructed, and this was his second mistake.

She had to differ enough so that the old goat would notice and desire her. A layer of fat was encased under the skin of her limbs to smooth out the bumps and make her legs more photogenic. Her frame was made more resilient and shock-proof, and better materials were used for her upholstery. Those nasty blemishes on Adam's bosom were streamlined and given a function. And on the off-chance that she might be turned into a monkey at the last minute, her genital organs were hooked to ligaments and muscles which would have worked wonderfully in a four-footed animal, but which proved next to useless in an erect female.

The canal through which future generations were to pass on the birth journey was modeled along the lines of a modern tunnel of love in a penny arcade—all planes and angles. (Many a medical student has been known to murmur in his fitful sleep, "Oh, why didn't they use zippers?")

Her thigh bones were so attached to the pelvis that her knees knocked together when she walked, and she was forced to slide them by each other with a swivel motion which was transmitted to the upper part of this long bone and to the muscles attached to it. This gave a peculiar motion to her *derrière,* which the male never tires of observing and admiring even more than such other natural phenomena as sunsets or Niagara Falls.

Man was endowed with all the sweet features of a Jersey bull's temperament; he charged everything in his path, head down, pawing, snorting and bellowing. But woman was given the guile of a bird-hunting cat, plus the cat's ability to keep out of awkward situations.

He was meant to dream and she was designed to dismiss his visions as hooey, being more interested in neighborhood chit-chat and in what man called on what frau than in who lit the stars at night and extinguished them in the morning.

Nature, not too proud of its first model, made an excess of him, to allow for breakage in delivery. It takes all the doctor's skill and a lot of endurance on Mom's part if her first-born is a boy, while girl babies are bonus jobs for us obstetricians.

Girls welcome their launching into a new world, but boys object to being so rudely ejected from the warm and comfortable nest of pregnancy. Girls are quickly adorned with beautiful pink ribbons and blankets, while the male child has to suffer a pruning operation on his most important organ before he can have his nakedness covered from the amused eyes of bystanders.

Once cradled in his mother's arms, the male finds his idea of heaven, and for the rest of his life he will try to get back to that womb-like protection. He enjoys her jealous possessiveness until the time when he wants younger arms around him. This yearning causes all kinds of trouble.

He belongs to his mother first. When he begins to notice his father at all, it is as a rival for his mother's affections, and, since poor Pop feels the same way about him, there is little love lost between them during the first year or two.

Then the relationship changes, and gradually the man buried within him begins to reach out to his father. Although the child will always regard his mother as a model of all that is good, virtuous and compassionate, Pop becomes his god, and Junior will crave both love and punishment from him.

This is the time for you to become a man, Dad. You will never be given a more apt and eager understudy than your own little boy. He is your most precious possession, but you will own him for such a little while. . . . A child is completely your own only at the moment of birth. So mold him, Pop, while he is pliable.

If you are neglectful about, or incapable of, molding your boy into a man, may the good Lord have mercy on you both.

2 The war of the sexes begins

Children begin by loving their parents; as they grow older they judge them; sometimes they forgive them.

OSCAR WILDE

Don't worry if your love for the new arrival seems shabby compared with the affection shown by his mother, and check that tomcat-like impulse to chew off his head when he cries with colic in the wee hours.

You must get used to the state of fatherhood by degrees. His mother's love has been building up for nine long months, while all you felt was resentment toward anything that could make her look so ridiculous. Now that she seems to have time for nobody except the baby, your feelings toward him have turned to jealousy. You also feel self-pity.

A mother's love flows toward the most helpless, and when the second baby arrives, you and the older child will find yourselves in the same boat—united by a common misery.

Sometimes the awareness of this comes all at once, as it did in my case. Our oldest son, who was two and a half when his brother was born, had acquired the habit of climbing out of his crib and sneaking in with his mother around midnight. I had never encouraged him to sleep with me, because he usually acted out that wonderful poem by Eugene Field, entitled "When Willie Wet the Bed."

While his mother was in the hospital he prudently stuck to his own sleeping quarters, but the first night she was home he searched for those comforting arms.

The new baby had colic most of the night, and when the little boy reached his mother's room he found her asleep with another boy cuddled in arms he had come to think were his very own.

I found him sobbing beside my bed, cold and most unhappy. When I asked why he was crying, he said, "There just ain't any place for Joe Peck any more."

He promised to refrain from wetting the bed, and pretty soon two lonesome guys were cuddling down together.

Was my love for my child born that night? I don't think so, but the realization of it was; for all love, save that resulting from passion, grows from the knowledge that the one loved needs and depends on the lover.

My second child never knew the misery connected with being superseded by a new love, and our mutual affection was of a more gradual flowering, but the need of a baby boy for a father's love and attention was soon impressed on me.

Somewhere between the ages of two and three the child begins to realize that he is of the male sex, and to look on men as superior beings. At this point, his father takes on the most important duty of his entire life.

The child's new awareness is due not only to his male inheritance, but also to the attitude adults have toward him. As a baby, he had learned to expect every woman to make a great fuss over him, and by the time he was a year old had found all this baby talk boring. As months pass, his reactions toward this treatment become more hostile, and by the time he is two years old he avoids strange women by hiding behind his mother's skirts. And the strange women often avoid him as though he were a leper.

At this stage he discovers that men, who had once looked at him from a sense of duty only, are beginning to return his questioning smile. Besides, they smell of tobacco and other interesting things. They let him make his advances as he sees fit, and they don't smear his face with nasty old lipstick or bore him with baby talk.

A child of two, like a dog, can read emotions in a stranger's face in one quick glance. He knows when he can expect a friendly pat or a kick in the slats. In fact, even a baby shows by his expression that he can tell the difference between what is said to him lovingly or in a scolding manner, and he can do this a long time before he understands what is being said. Young children have an amazing ability to connect fleeting facial expressions and other gestures to thoughts and emotions.

I once saw a beautiful demonstration of a child's attitude toward the two sexes, with my older son as the principal actor. I had been called back to Missouri because of illness in the family, and, since we had a new baby, my wife thought it best to stay home. The older child, who was nearly three, begged so hard I took him on the three-day train ride.

Because of a wreck west of Ogden, Utah, our east-bound train had few passengers, and all those in the Pullman section were men.

Before we reached Wyoming, my boy had investigated the pockets of every man in the observation car. Tiring of that, he played train with the vacant seats in the car. The conductor and flagman joined him, and soon every man aboard was either a passenger or a member of the crew. Those who didn't feel up to chugging, whistling or going ding-ding were the passengers, gravely tearing off pieces of newspapers or magazines so their tickets would be ready when the little conductor came by, which he did every five minutes. This play continued until about five o'clock, when my boy got tired and hungry.

The steward then carried him into the dining car on his shoulders and the chef prepared his supper early so he could go to bed. The steward then informed the rest of us that if we wanted any food that night we'd better come along and eat with the youngster. Not one word of protest, and thus did one little boy achieve the ambition of all little boys, as well as big ones: he ran a Union Pacific passenger train to suit himself.

On the return trip the train was jammed with women. Two, who were schoolmarms on their way to a Colorado vacation, had the berth above ours. Before we had left the yards of Kansas City they were worrying about the little boy rubbing against their skirts as he played in his half of the section, audibly wondering whether he would wake up early and spoil their beauty sleep, which they looked as if they needed.

Two men across the aisle who overheard them accosted me later in the diner and suggested a trade. One, who snored in several keys, was pretty certain that he could keep the frosty spinsters entertained all though the night instead of only after daylight. The other gent was a sound sleeper who said he arose early anyway, and he agreed to switch berths. When the two gals heard of the arrangement, they perked up and even smiled at my little boy.

My confederate across the aisle didn't underestimate his ability to make the night musical. And, my son, awakening at dawn, looked out the window and called my attention to every colt and lamb he saw. I was still tired and sleepy, and was glad when the early riser took my boy out to the observation car, remarking that he would like to see the breaking day once more through a child's wondering eyes.

At breakfast we sat across the table from the two teachers, who looked weary and wan. I set the boy's glass of milk in position so that if he knocked it over it would spill in their direction. Unfortunately, his table manners were unusually good that morning.

Again he made friends with all the men in the car, but he didn't favor a single (or married) woman with a friendly look. He was a boy, now, and would never again look upon any woman but his mother as a friend until circumstances beyond his control forced him to accept his schoolteachers.

Women despise children who aren't dependent on them, and men like boys because they can look back on their childhood days with fond memories that are easily revived when there is a small boy around. Women would be more acceptable if they were a bit less overdone when they reach the prime of life.

Men realize early that they are incomplete organisms who must have a god to worship—one whom they can endow with all the powers they lack.

First, it's a man's mother. Then, for a few years, Dad is supreme, and after him come football coaches, prizefighters and other athletic heroes. Then some girl; and when the young man finds that girls are merely human like himself, he turns to the supernatural.

If there were no true God, man would fashion one out of stone or wood to fill his need.

3 *The child's side, your side, and the backside*

Boys are found everywhere—on top of, underneath, inside of, climbing on, swinging from, running around, or jumping to. Mothers love them, little girls hate them, older sisters and brothers tolerate them. . . .

ALAN BECK

Around the age of four or five a boy gets his first taste of the frustrations that will dog him for years. He plays with little girls of his own age.

They may take turns being doctor, nurse and patient, in which case they will take wondering peeks at each other's anatomy. Girls may also initiate him into the rites of keeping house, and the shocks connected therewith make him gun shy and contribute to his future tendency to shirk domestic responsibility, for when he plays a major role in these make-believes he is promptly squelched and bawled out by the more precocious females.

Fancying herself an expert on biology, she tells him tartly

that her sex is supreme, that she alone can carry babies in her stomach and that his job is to bring home groceries. She scolds him for waking her dolls and says things that give him a feeling of inferiority.

This minor role dismays him. For one thing, the belief that the stork or doctor brings babies is more firmly rooted in his mind than is his faith in Santa Claus. Of course he knows that cats have kittens and that dogs have puppies, but to connect himself and his mother with such a messy process is more than his growing masculinity can accept. Never will he witness the birth of a child in after years if he can possibly avoid it.

Man doesn't like to be reminded that he is actually a member of the weaker sex, which he is. He is, after all, the sum total of countless generations of males whose responsibility to camp or community included fathering children, killing for food, and fighting neighbors. All these things show up in his genes.

Some day he will be civilized enough to accept commonplace chores, but there are many rebellions between childhood and man's estate.

If normal, he may gather a few pals, attack the playhouse gang, scalp the dolls and, if matches are handy, maybe burn down the playhouse. If so, punish him, Pop.

One thing that makes a boy lose interest in the playhouse is the realism of the toys; the dolls cry, go to sleep, and sometimes wet their pants. The cook stoves look like mother's. Girls like them that way, but boys, more visionary, want their toys simple so that they can use their imagination in dealing with them. The less the toys resemble the picture in their mind, the more room there is for their imagination to take over. Did you ever see a little boy pick a piece of cake out of a magazine and offer the mythical morsel to his parents' guests?

When my sons were six and four, respectively, I bought them the best train I could find in a bargain basement. After playing with it for one day, they shoved it into a corner, and there it stayed until their mother put it away. The following Christmas season, the younger boy wrote Santa, asking for a train he could push while doing his own chuffing and tooting—and his own wrecking when he was so inclined.

Their heroes were Rikki-tikki-tavi, the Indian mongoose in Kipling's *Jungle Book,* and Jim Hawkins in *Treasure Island,* while that of my grandson seems to be the bold and brave cowpoke who rights all wrongs, kills ten bad men with one six-shooter, and never gets hitched or becomes a papa.

So don't expect your little son to gurgle with joy over the fancy toys you buy him. That replica of your new car is indeed beautiful, but he would prefer to receive four old baby buggy wheels and a few scraps of two-by-fours. To be real foxy, hide them in the garden house and let him discover them for himself. From them he will construct a wagon, a wonderful vehicle whose wheels slant in different directions. Coming down the driveway, it looks like a fiddler crab uncertain just what direction to try next. He made it with his own hands, however; therefore it is beautiful, and his imagination will fit it with dream gadgets not yet conceived by industrial engineers.

He loves to play with a pistol he made out of wood, clothespins and rubber bands, and his eyes will truly shine when he first holds his own fishing rod or a .410-gauge shotgun. Go as far as you like when you buy that gun. He *will* take care of it.

Don't call your boy a baby if he riots when confronted by a doctor with a hypodermic full of diphtheria toxoid or some other immunizing agent. Girls like to be hurt a little, but boys and men are desperately afraid of needles.

In training camp during the first World War, I saw many a

dignified physician faint and fall like a poled ox when he saw the needle approaching his arm, and most of them sneaked out behind the infirmary and bathed their smallpox vaccination with alcohol to kill the virus before it was absorbed, thereby avoiding the possibility of a sore arm.

Let nature take its course. Suppose your youngster does bite his fingernails and pick his nose when nervous about something; next week he'll be cracking his knuckles and the third week he'll have a brand new annoying habit. That is, unless you have scolded him about the first ones, in which case he'll still be biting and picking.

Ignore such things and he will quickly forget them. If he wets his bed, praise him when he *does not,* and encourage him to try harder the next night if he fails. Don't punish him for any of these things whatever you do, but lay on the hand when he knowingly disobeys you. He will do this, if for no other reason than to test you out.

For the good of society he should be spanked when necessary during his early years when his natural instincts must be repressed. As someone said, there are three sides to discipline: the child's side, the parents' side, and the side that should be spanked. And when you spank your boy, go at it as if you were killing snakes. He will enjoy the show and appreciate the paddling, and it will be good for his ego. Always temper your discipline with common sense, however. There will be times when his mother, giving way to her natural maternal solicitude to shield him from this cruel world, will unwisely recommend clemency. If so, send her to a quiet spot where she can't hear the spanking. Criminals are often made by overly protective mothers who don't realize that a son is a chunk of metal fresh from the furnace and needs an abrasive to polish him off.

Like you, your son expects his god to be just—one who will reward him when he obeys the commandments and punish him when he doesn't. We love our Creator more when His face seems to be turned from us, and are more apt to backslide when things seem to be going along nicely and we get away with things for which we know we should incur His wrath.

My professional life was cursed by a few mothers who read too many misguiding guidance books. Instead of raising their kids as nature intended, they worried about the shock to the youngsters' nervous systems should they give way to the impulse to spank them. When they brought these unruly brats into my office, I turned them over on my knee and administered a therapeutic dose of what they had been missing. The mothers were horrified, but the kids regarded me as a second father and thereafter became most cooperative patients.

Don't, of course, over-do this just-and-noble father stuff. Your child, knowing that you are human, will overlook minor lapses from the ideal and love you all the more for them. Just as adults scorn the perfect little touch-me-not, so does a child get bored with too much goodness and right.

I lay down the ideal, but I never attained it, and I don't expect you to do so. Should any Pop qualify as nearly perfect, his offspring would probably develop into a fiend to balance the equation. Just try to be the best father possible and the day will come when your kids will love and respect you more than you deserve.

The little fellows realize their helplessness and insecurity almost from the day of birth, and nothing so upsets their world as domestic strife or emotional tension. Remember that a child is a dependent creature who for years gropes around in a world of giants. Also, that when they pass through annoying stages it is just another example of history repeating itself. You were once a brat yourself, and if you succeeded in growing up you're lucky.

A break-up in the home can be disastrous for your young son. If this catastrophe is the result of death, the child reacts

I administered a therapeutic dose of what he had been missing.

much differently than in the case of divorce. Here he feels a sense of responsibility toward the remaining parent and may well develop into a better man than if his father lived. But where parents are separated, he is burdened with a sense of shame and degradation, and almost always develops an inferiority complex in dealing with children from happy homes.

No stepfather or stepmother can remove the blight on his development. So even if you have to take guff from your mother-in-law, stay with your boy until he is old enough to navigate by himself. Otherwise you will spoil two men's lives and benefit nobody. Most of all, you will break your covenant with your God to love and cherish the little life He has entrusted to your care.

When Darwin was asked in which three years of his life a man learned the most, he said: "The first three." By the time your boy is ten he has learned more than he will absorb during the rest of his life. The period between two and ten puts an especially mighty burden on a father's shoulders, because being a god is a pretty exacting job—one that carries with it more responsibilities than most fathers can meet. Yet he must face up to the job or fail in the most important mission for which he was placed on earth.

Mother can raise daughters and comfort and bind up the wounds of their sons, but the man-plan that boys follow is inscribed on their brain cells by the manner in which Pop conducts himself before them and by the just punishments he inflicts when they get out of line.

Sons of fathers who were poor gods have become great, and some attain greatness without a father's guidance, but for the average boy to develop into a law-abiding citizen, a father's example and precept is a must.

Impressions have been crowding one another as they registered on the fast-growing baby brain, and it is during this period of increasing worship for the father (while the mother becomes progressively less important except when he wants something or wishes to have his ruffled feelings soothed) that the foundations of character are laid. What Pop does will be the blueprint for the building of his son's character.

If he brags about sharp practices at the dinner table, his son believes forever after that to skin a sucker is perfectly legitimate.

If he fibs to the cop who stopped him for speeding, his son will disregard Sunday School teachers who say lying is sinful; and if the old man runs through a stop-light while Junior is in the car, traffic lights become something to ignore if you can get away with it.

If father is gentle and considerate with mother, his son will without question treat all her sex with consideration. Be unjust and domineering toward your wife, Pop, and your daughters-in-law will be justified in cursing the day you were born.

Drink to excess before your son and he will think drinking is smart. Because of you, alcohol assumes a glamor that is hard to forget, and he may wind up on skid row because of your thoughtfulness.

Drag your son along when you visit art galleries or museums and explain as best you can the story of past greatness. Take him to see good shows that have withstood the test of time and he will be more apt to enjoy them when he gets big enough to understand them. My younger son was five when he first saw *Romeo and Juliet*, and he convulsed the audience around us when he inquired as the first curtain fell: "Papa, is this like church, or do you clap your hands?" I can remember our boys sitting in our laps when we saw *The Bohemian Girl*, and I still recall what a local theatre manager told me a couple of years later. He could always tell, he said, when he had a clinker at the Saturday matinee: my kids usually walked out before the first act was over.

Leave good books and magazines scattered around the living room and give your boy books on his birthday anniversaries and at Christmas—books that have delighted boys for generations. Although he will devote a large part of his time to comics, he will, without extra effort on your part, come to realize that he is wasting his time on such reading and will cultivate a taste for what is proper for a developing mind. I heard of one ten-year-old whose mother was cleaning out some of his trashy comic books. "Don't throw that one away, Mom," he said. "That's the one on torturing women." Parents have themselves to blame if the taste of their kids doesn't develop properly.

If you must read best-selling novels, hide them under the mattress until Junior is asleep. Children will soon enough find out about rape, incest, and murder without having it crammed into their little brains at home. Not that a list of best-sellers isn't useful in later life as a guide to what not to read.

A little boy's mind is like a garden; the seeds you plant therein grow either into weeds or flowers, and both are hard to dig out.

One thing your boy will cherish above all else is that hunting or fishing trip he made with you; so, even though he may be a nuisance who has to be carried over streams and wire fences, include him whenever possible in such male outings. There is something about these purely masculine rites in fields and woods that cements a fellowship between father and son. It's an experience never to be forgotten by either, and it gives you a chance, if your boy is old enough to need it, to sneak in a lot of advice. This is saying a good deal, as most fathers know.

Until they are old enough to expect to find human nature a bit frail about obeying laws, however, be careful of your adult companions. Once I was with a party hunting pheasants when one of the men killed a hen, though hens were out of season at all times. Later, when we stopped for a smoke, I overheard two small boys discussing the incident.

"Why did Mr. Jones shoot that hen?" one said. "Will Papa report him to the game warden?"

"Well," the older child said, "Mr. Jones wears glasses and can't see as well as the rest of us. Besides, we were yelling at the dog, so maybe he didn't hear it when it flew up."

I was glad that my own sons weren't along, for I wouldn't have enjoyed trying to cover the clay feet of one of their virile idols.

By the way, don't take women on these nature trips. They ruin the communion which is rare between father and son, and which flowers with its greatest magnificence when they are together in the silent wilderness, "God's first temples."

Today, when my children bring their families to our woodsy little farm for holidays, we men leave the wives and grandchildren at the house, and, equipped with saw and axe, wander down into the woods with the avowed intention of cutting wood for the fireplace. We each cut one piece and squat on it, light our smokes, and try to recreate the spell we used to enjoy on the streams and in the fields of their native Utah. I am not enough of an egotist to think that they accept the advice I hand down from my Nebo-like perch on the biggest log, but at least they pretend to listen.

A boy who grows up without warm associations with his father is denied his birthright.

4

Are your genes showing?

Standing with reluctant feet,
Where the brook and river meet,
Womanhood and childhood fleet!
HENRY WADSWORTH LONGFELLOW

Longfellow mixed his sexes. In my medical experience I never saw a girl whose feet showed any reluctance when the time came for her to step into the river of womanhood. In fact, instead of reluctantly accepting the process, many girls try to give the illusion of advancing development by stuffing things into the front of their dresses so that their bosoms will approximate the ideal of beauty so cherished by movie directors and dairymen. This gives them that forward look.

Girls have always looked forward to destiny. It is the boy whose feet are reluctant when he finds himself standing where the brook and the river meet. He tries to ignore the river.

A boy from ten to thirteen is something nobody but a mother could love. Half the time he even hates himself.

While a girl becomes more graceful and attractive, a boy grows more awkward and more conscious of his clumsiness. A fuzzy growth appears on his face. Whiskers, starting singly and in pairs, soon grow rapidly, curling as they grow. When he can stand his appearance no longer, he sneaks into the bathroom and shaves with his father's razor. The minute he gets to school some girl yodels, "Willie has had a shave!" Had she yelled, "Willie has finally washed his neck!" his confusion and shame could not have been greater, and he is tempted to run away from home.

Acne pimples sprout where whiskers don't; his nose gets big and his feet smelly. He becomes discouraged and careless, dressing even more slovenly than you thought possible. And he talks a jargon like nothing Webster ever heard.

At this time he undergoes quick reversals. One minute he cries like a baby, the next he is so grown up and dignified he makes you feel like a child. He starts a sentence in a childish soprano and finishes it like a bullfrog with laryngitis. Nature is using her invisible hypodermic to inject progressively stronger doses of male sex hormone into his veins, and his reactions are constantly swinging from desire for violent bodily contact with his fellows to a strange lassitude. He may show up at the breakfast table with a shiner or some other evidence of physical combat, and you must realize that there is a time for fighting and a time to refrain from fighting. Your son must expect his share of bumps and lumps, and if he gets into trouble let him pay the piper.

At this stage he obeys you because the pattern is hard to break, and, besides, he is not quite sure he can lick you. But there will come a time when he can tell the old man to go to hell, and that is one of his sweetest dreams. His animosity toward his father grows as his sex develops, and they can never meet again on common ground until he has kids of his own.

By accident he discovers the relief afforded by masturbation, but that, too, reacts like a ton of fireworks going off in his head. I recall a medical student who claimed he had been destined to be a ballet dancer. His first experience with this type of relief occurred behind a haystack, and he swore that for ten minutes he fluttered around that stack on the tips of his toes, performing all the graceful gyrations of the wounded bird in *Swan Lake*.

The first act of masturbation transforms a simple, direct, honest youngster into a dual personality. All boys practice it, and they all lie about it. As a result, your little son has a deep and awful secret which he is sure will undermine his reason and health. The unaccustomed effort to carry two personalities probably does the most harm, for now he must cultivate a face to present to the rest of humanity and try to suppress the man he knows he is. Unfortunately, this burden weighs him down throughout life.

By this time his mother is suspecting things, and she has been hounding the old man to talk to Junior. Now the fat is in the fire. Father would rather go into the ring and fight a bull without a sword than do this, and Junior probably wishes he would do so and get gored for his pains. In this respect, a physician is better situated than most men. I well remember when my wife insisted that I go through this ordeal. One Sunday morning I told the boys we were going to my office for a little talk. They exchanged knowing glances, wondering what the old man had found out now.

I reached for a book on obstetrics and started my lecture. My younger son politely walked over to look out the window, while the older boy sat, blushed, and squirmed. I icily inquired if I was boring them.

"Papa," my older son said, "we have known all about that

as long as I can remember. Our first picture book was your old Gray's Anatomy, and we often hear you talking to patients over the phone."

"Let's go fishing and tell mother it took a long time to educate you," I said.

But I didn't get out of it quite that easily. The Mormons believe in practical religion, and, although I was a Gentile, they asked me to lecture to a class of young boys on the facts of life.

I faced a dozen youngsters, who were all trying to hide their embarrassment by acting as if I weren't there. After talking for a few minutes, I realized that I was getting further and further from my audience, so I asked if there were any questions.

"Let's talk about breeding rabbits," one bright youngster said. "I've got a doe that won't have babies."

From then on my class was a big success, until a supervisor dropped in one day and found that his facts-of-life program had turned into a veterinary clinic.

The money problem also confronts Pop at this time. Teenage sons look upon fathers as a tree that sheds money. Provide them only with necessities and pay for their education if you can. Never give them a dime for fun unless they do something to earn it.

A grandson of Brigham Young, the Mormon leader, told me that his father, who had raised several boys, paid them the going wages to dig deep holes in the backyard. If they wanted more money, he paid them half-time to fill in the holes—never giving them a cent more, no matter how they pleaded.

The chief job of society is to find an outlet for the excessive energy generated at this stage of a boy's development. I'm glad that my boys were at this adolescent period before all those child labor laws went into effect. I sent them to C.M.T.C., where they learned the rudiments of self-preservation; I let them work at the smelter, where they expended their energy on an eight-pound hammer making little pieces of slag out of big ones; and I made them work in the garden, although their mother often had to stand by and point to every weed before they would pull it out.

Our grandfathers kept their sons busy clearing land or they bound them out to learn a trade. In their homespun days, each individual had a stake in providing food for the family. When I was a boy there was always wood to cut and rabbits to hunt. The devil finds work for idle hands, but my hands were kept fairly busy. In our modern civilization, what is there for a youngster to do?

He lives on a tiny lot in a house with automatic heat. No wood to chop and a power mower for his lawn. When he gets too old for things such as scouting, just what in hell is he going to do? Probably gang up with his idle friends and roam the neighborhood in search of any kind of excitement to combat boredom, and a neighborhood gang can be as destructive as a bunch of sheep-killing dogs.

Whenever I see a gang of youngsters hanging around, I am reminded of an article Albert Payson Terhune wrote about his collie dogs. He was famous as a breeder of this beautiful but useless creature, and one day he came home just as a herder was driving a flock of sheep down the road with the help of a couple of ordinary sheep dogs. He said that the longing shown in the eyes of those fancy collies made him swear never again to raise as a house pet a dog that was meant for work.

In our new-found wisdom we have passed child labor laws that prevent children from doing anything useful and almost force them to become a delinquency problem for the community. Child labor in sweat shops, of course, was a disgrace, but so is the fact that millions of young American men must live through summers wandering around, listless and unproductive, and often presenting behavior problems.

I feel sorry for the father confronted by this problem, but sorrier for his sons, for they are big enough to realize their potential. They long to be engaged in some constructive labor and they know that society has legislated them out of the herd. And to feel unwanted is an awful thing—a problem many old folks know too well.

Add to this the awakening of a boy's sex drives. This, when not balanced by hard manual labor, is enough to drive even well-adjusted youngsters nuts.

The unoccupied adolescent turns to sex to relieve boredom. I ask you to remember the wild dreams and impulses that bedeviled you once you got the woodbox full and had nothing much to do. Remember the embarrassing erections that came at the most unfortunate moments? You imagined that everyone noticed the disarrangement of your trousers, and perhaps you recall shoving your fist into your pocket to keep people from thinking you had a corncob concealed therein.

If your boy was raised right during his first twelve or thirteen years, he will somehow worry through the tough period of adolescence. The thirteen-to-seventeen age bracket presents acute problems, and just how you are going to solve them is a fair question. The lamb in wolf's clothing during these years becomes a wolf in lamb's clothing, and your boy may become a problem to your community as well as to you.

In his upbringing you were handicapped almost from the beginning by Washington bureaucrats who converted the period of adolescence into a paying business. Many of these bureaucrats are self-appointed messiahs who don't know enough to raise turnips, let alone families. It was a mistake for them to sweep under the rug all the accumulated wisdom of the ages.

Years ago a bunch of old biddies, probably thwarted in their natural desire for motherhood, took over the children's bureau in Washington and sold a bill of goods that it was an antiquated notion to think that parents could raise their own offspring during the tender, twig-straightening years. These biddies were so far removed from reality they didn't understand, for example, that as far as growing children are concerned they prefer to fight their own battles rather than be coddled and treated like hot-house plants.

A whole new way of life was opened for career women who could not make a success of anything else, and parents were hounded to distraction by welfare workers, well-baby and well-child clinics, child-guidance clinics, and God knows what else.

Efforts were and are being made to regulate the baby's upbringing almost to the point where the child is taken from his home in birth and raised according to regulations thought up by crackpot child psychologists.

How serene life would be if we could ship all our do-gooders and uplifters off to enlighten heathen savages instead of having to suffer the consequences of their misguided efforts to remake our own world.

Once your son attains adolescence, he is in the same fix as a half-grown dog. Everybody loved and wanted to cuddle him when he was a puppy, but now that he is big enough to knock over the goldfish bowl and your favorite golf trophy, he lands in the dog pound, or, at best, gets a swift kick in the stern.

But despair not, Pop, your offspring may be a trial to his family, school and community, but just remember that he was created in the image of his Maker. Comfort yourself with the thought that some day he may show some of the worthy characteristics he inherited.

But meanwhile, a lot of fathers are worried, and they have good reason. They are worried because their genes are beginning to show. . . .

5

"I zink maybe I don't know"

Something depressing comes on the mind when it has been too extensively occupied with the female sex.

JAMES STEPHENS

During adolescence the female sex engrosses most of the waking moments (and some of the sleeping moments) of your son. Pleasant dreams, as well as nightmares, are connected with the problem.

One of my duties as superintendent of the medical department of an Anaconda Copper plant was to examine European immigrants who were looking for jobs. The second question on the questionnaire was age, and here things often got fouled up, even though the questions were asked through an interpreter.

The interpreter would turn to the applicant and wave his arms and jabber, whereupon the bewildered gink would spread out his hands and shrug helplessly, a tortured look in his eyes. Then the go-between would turn to me with some evasive answer.

I would pound the table and yell again, and the interpreter would go through more calisthenics and rave some more. Finally a look of understanding would come over the poor applicant's face, and he would yammer a bit. At this point the interpreter generally gave me a stock answer: "He zink maybe he don't know."

As far as the adolescent period from thirteen to seventeen is concerned, I zink maybe I don't know. No man living knows more about adolescent boys than I, and I know nothing.

But I do know that internal secretions of the male sex glands at this time are adding more and more drive to the boy's impulses, and the steering mechanism is still subject to breakdowns. He resents efforts of his elders to assist in piloting his craft, although to adult eyes he seems to be sailing in aimless circles.

The female of the species begins to attract him, and to get her attention he borrows the courting methods of the rooster sage chicken. He struts around ignoring her presence while performing every ridiculous stunt he can think up.

At this period he is so purely masculine he won't even wash his face or comb his hair. But this stage, too, will pass, and as he succumbs to the influence of girls, he is liable to try to remove his freckles with carbolic acid.

Girls, meanwhile, take care of the dating technique. How they tame him and put the first halter over his head is beyond his comprehension, but they do it.

When the boy begins dating, a whole new set of problems arises, bringing new worries to banish sleep. My wife's philosophy is, I think, the best to tide you over this hurdle.

I awoke one midnight to find her coming to bed. When I asked why the delay, she said that our older son had not come home from a date, and she had been worried about him. I asked her why, since he was still missing, she was going to bed after sitting up half the night.

"I refuse to worry after midnight," she said. "Let the girl's mother take it from there."

I must depend now on my own experience as a boy and on clinical impressions gathered over the years, because no man ever hears about his son's escapades except by accident, and then usually from some loose-tongued gossip.

In dealing with juvenile problems I formed a wholesome respect for the natural chastity of the young male. Believe me, adolescent boys seldom are the intentional aggressors in the game of sex at this time.

They tend to relieve their animal tensions by self-abuse, and in so doing down-grade themselves and come to look upon all females as pure and as holy as mothers of the race are supposed to be.

Boys are as shy as rabbits, because any sex jam is sure to be blamed on them, and man's code demands that he will not defend himself when a woman's honor is concerned.

Instinct teaches boys to be the aggressors, but most of them draw a line beyond which they will think long and hard before passing over. Even though they find it more and more difficult to postpone sexual satisfaction, feelings of guilt and fear come into play. They worry about the possibility of being discovered or of contracting a venereal disease, and the thought of getting a chick pregnant is enough to drive them daffy. But if circumstances beyond their control make them cross the Rubicon, they try to be nonchalant about it.

They could, like Joseph of the Old Testament, run. Some of them do, but, unlike that old savage, they don't tell about it later. (I sometimes wonder whether Moses didn't just pick that story out of the air to glamorize his kinfolk. He was a natural-born yarn-spinner, and since all of the Potiphar family were dead, like any historian he cared little about anyone not

When the boy begins dating, a whole new set of problems arises.

around to sue him. But if the story is true, Joseph was some heel, as well as being a sharp cookie at rent collecting. (Incidentally, I still think it was Joseph's pants, not his cloak, that Mrs. Potiphar had to explain to the old man.)

I had one experience somewhat similar to Joseph's but my reputation was ruined. Had I followed Joseph's example, I could have been hung on circumstantial evidence.

When seventeen, I visited a pal whose girl got a date for me, and we went out for the evening. We soon paired off, and since it was a beautiful moonlit summer night, my girl and I took a walk. I didn't know the town and let her pick the way. Moments later we were strolling down a deserted country lane.

After walking about a mile she suggested that we rest under a tree where the grass was nice and clean. I, thinking about grass stain and chiggers (nasty little insects that live in the grass of the Mid-West and burn like fury when they burrow under the skin), hunted up a couple of rocks to sit on. Ignoring hers, she flopped full length on the grass and suggested that I do likewise. But being a stranger and on my good behavior, I sat on the rock. Besides, I hated chiggers. I wasn't exactly a rube, but I didn't want to get involved in anything too serious, so I acted as though I thought her truly tired and let her rest.

She quickly recovered, and we headed back. At her front door I figured that perhaps I'd better assert myself and steal a goodnight kiss, as was expected from knights errant in such circumstances. Instead of the friendly wrestle I expected, she swung one from the hip and blacked my eye good and proper.

I didn't blame her too much. After all, it was a long walk to waste on a guy who was so blind to his opportunities, but the evidence next day, which I couldn't hide, branded me as a wolf and her as a brave little girl who could protect her honor.

My name is Joseph, but hers was definitely not Mrs. Potiphar. I said nothing to defend myself, but I did get even with her sex during ensuing years. Whenever boy-girl problems came to my office, I judged the gal guilty until it was clearly proved otherwise.

A boy is really behind the eight-ball in these affairs, and if anyone should stand by him and try to understand his predicament it is his father.

Although he will later in bull sessions boast of the number of gals he has seduced (while women brag about the number of Romeos they have thwarted), he won't discuss his troubles with you or anybody else. You must accordingly treat him as a man and use all the art of a glib salesman to get him to listen to you. Here is your chance to take him on one of those camping safaris, but be sure you give him the impression that he is going along just to have fun and maybe to keep bears from feasting on you.

Some night around the camp fire begin your own confessional. Instead of asking him about his troubles, tell him what a ninny you were at his age. There will be a similarity, despite the fact that you belong to an earlier generation. The human race doesn't change that fast.

He may not open up, but at least he will laugh with you at the figure you cut, and he will apply some of your solutions to his own case. Senator Beveridge of Indiana once remarked that a young man needed a moral bath on Sunday as badly as he needed an external one Saturday night. It made little difference, he said, what church he attended, or whether he believed a word he heard; but the associations and atmosphere in the house of worship would purge his soul and he would leave a better and more understanding man than when he entered.

I tried his method, and it helped, though perhaps not enough to arouse comment from my acquaintances.

You should, without letting your son suspect it, give him a moral bath or at least an escape hatch for his feelings of guilt and shame. At the camp fire describe the satisfactions of going with four or five dames at the same time, implying that this going-steady racket is more unnatural for a boy than a ducktail haircut. Say it is nothing but a female form of social security that robs him of all the fun of being a boy and that makes him an old man before his time.

You and I know that men with enough drive to make a success in the business world also have to struggle to keep their marriage vows. Why should a child be saddled with a similar responsibility?

His Maker meant for him to be wild and free for a while before becoming a man in fact as well as fancy. If he doesn't sow a few wild oats now, he surely will later, when harvesting the crop will be more of a calamity. Accept the fact that he is quite likely to get into the shotgun-wedding category before he has learned to shave.

Modern girls may be smarter than their parents, but mistakes happen, and they do get pregnant in the same old way as Eve. The one great law in sex play is progression; each time the boy begins where he left off last time, and he goes as far as the girl will let him. If he doesn't make progress each time, both of them will be disappointed; and if they go steady, it won't be long before there will be no more worlds left to conquer.

Thus, if he is engaged in several campaigns at the same time, his efforts will be scattered over a wider field, and he is less likely to hit paydirt in any one scrimmage.

Remind your son that girls are not cast from the same mold, that he will never know what he wants in a wife until he has explored the field. And then, if he gets into a jam, let him suffer the consequences even if it means his spending a night in jail.

Expect him to make mistakes, but if you would have him avoid those you made, tell him about them and don't spare your reputation. By now you are no longer a god, but just another guy who has traveled this same road, and a person who knows where most of the mud holes are because you fell into them.

Some anonymous sage said that life resembles a one-way street in two respects: You are not coming back, and a lot of people on it are going in the wrong direction.

You owe it to your boy to start him off on the right track.

6

Of mice and women

Whoever heard of a mousetrap chasing a mouse?

ANONYMOUS

A girl thirteen or fourteen years old and a boy of seventeen are about equally developed in their desires.

She is happy if she has a horse to ride. And if she has boys to practice her new mouse-catching game on, she is in clover.

The boy's idea of heaven is a hot-rod with an open muffler and pretty girls to take riding therein, for at this age a normal lad is more than ever capable of loving with all his heart several girls at the same time.

At this time of life society expects him to act the part of a wild young stallion running the ridges and neighing his defiance to all the world as he tries to set up housekeeping with every filly he meets.

If halter-broken at this age, your son has whinnied down the wrong pasture. He has missed loads of fun and heartaches, too, which, in retrospect, are also fun.

Times and customs change, but human nature is pretty constant. When I was seventeen I would cheerfully saw wood all day Saturday to earn a dollar to spend on Sunday to hire a horse and buggy so I could take my crush of the moment riding for a few hours.

Why we went riding I don't recall, since the Missouri town we lived in was so small we could have walked to a lonesome, romantic spot in a few minutes, and riding in Missouri was just snailing down a dusty, ragweed-bordered lane between corn fields so high you couldn't see fifty feet on either side.

The horses were worth the money, however, because they were well informed on the ways of a man with a maid. In town they were spirited—heads high and tails streaming—but on a lonely road they could move at such a deliberate pace that no dust was kicked up to bother their passengers.

At the sound of an approaching vehicle they would dash out of the way as if going to a fire, and once out of the trail of dust would browse along the side of the road like a cow returning from pasture. And no man-made machine will ever guarantee that lovers will return from a journey as safely as those ponies returned us. In my day, of course, there were no prowl cars to hurry you on and no lovers'-lane bandits to make ardor flee.

Although the reins were wrapped around the whip-stand where they bothered neither horse nor paying guests, the horses avoided wayside trees, never missed a bridge, and never ran out of gas.

If the conversation was in normal tones, they tended to the business of traveling; if in soft, low murmurs, they made about a mile an hour; and if conversation stopped or was interrupted by the sound of lip-smacking, they paused to fight imaginary horseflies until invited to resume the journey.

Now in my old age, when I am once more cutting wood, I

don't regret spending my hard-earned money on so romantic a pastime.

During adolescence your boy has the soul of a poet and the carnal appetites of a tomcat, so it's no wonder his judgments are as erratic as his emotions. He buys one of those "I-love-you-truly" bracelets for his beloved one week and takes it back the following week to give it to a new-found love. As he approaches the advanced stage of adolescence, it is inevitable that with all his running around he will meet a girl who will take his puppy advances so seriously she will meet him more than half way.

Now he becomes a man via a christening which he will forever hide and try to forget, for added to the feelings of shame and guilt which he has about losing his own virginity and causing the gal to lose hers, perhaps, is the fear that his sexual awkwardness will make him the butt of her ridicule.

Soon after he has reached his new man status, he quits his sessions of self relief for his pent-up tensions and tries to rape every girl he meets, half hoping that he will be repulsed in his amorous endeavors. But too often he is not repelled, and he thereby gets disgusted with himself and with the girls who cooperate. His ideals have been shattered, his idols dragged in the dust. But his mother and the girls who resist him are enshrined deeper in his heart, thus making his mind a house divided against itself.

One day he is the cynical man of the world, the next day he longs to return to the status of the trustful little boy he once was. He loses faith easily. He finds out that one sanctimonious elder is a hypocritical fraud, so he loses faith in his church and its teachings.

He comes to think that all politics is crooked, and philanthropy is just a scheme to wangle money out of you. Good girls are fickle and after prospective husbands with money.

He has reached the stage where he doesn't give a damn, and now his whole being calls for action—maybe violent action.

He is in the perfect state to make a great soldier, anxious to vent his spleen and contempt on any adversary, and on the world in general. He may join or help organize some revolutionary movement in the interest of liberty, the extermination of cats or the unlimited manufacture of contraceptives. The goal is unimportant; it is the revolt that matters. He may attain a heroic stature only dreamed of by other less troubled men, as did the boys in Hungary, or he may land in jail for raiding a sorority in search of girl's panties, as sometimes happens on the college campus.

Besides joining crusades for lost causes and trying to right all the wrongs suffered by man and beast, a boy sixteen or seventeen years old may go through the experience of getting intoxicated. When our sons came home one night as drunk as hoot owls, my wife and I did not scold or weep, but I never will forget the therapeutic treatment their mother gave the younger one. Feeling a bit queasy the morning after, he asked for a bowl of milk toast. Mother gave him a covered dish, and when he removed the lid, he found nice brown pieces of toast floating around in steaming hot beer. And it was a case of eat or have it poured down your throat.

A father must also be firm in dealing with some of the other dangerous aspects of modern living. I allowed my sons to use the family car, but only with the understanding that they would be grounded if there were any dents or scraped paint. They might get hit from the rear, but it was up to them to avoid bridge railings, poles and oncoming cars. They knew I meant it, so there were no wrecks.

The only cure for your son at this stage is time.

While he ponders his future, you think of the little boy who begged Pop to read the funnies to him. He held your hand so tightly when you crossed the street, and his tiny arms were clasped around your neck when he rode piggy-back across streams too deep for his little boots. You taught him how to handle his gun, and you were so proud of him when he did well in school or in athletics. But most of all, perhaps, you remember times when he was sick and unhappy—when nothing comforted him quite so much as having you hold him in your arms and tell him stories about the time when you were a little boy yourself. . . .

That chapter is forever closed, but the memory of it will remain forever precious.

Some time during the latter part of his adolescence, Pop, depending on circumstances and the nature of your son, you should have acquainted him with the fundamental differences in the mating process between the sexes. It's natural for him to consider himself a free agent and to think that all his decisions are of his own making, but, as you know so well from experience, that is definitely not so when it comes to marriage.

In the eyes of the lover, says the proverb, pock marks are dimples. You may or may not have proposed to your wife. Chances are that you don't remember doing so, or of having had any intention of doing so. You may recall that you were mildly surprised to find yourself buying a ring.

Getting married is not a man's business, and he has received no training in the approach to this situation. He expects to get hitched some day, since it is the thing to do, but as in joining a church, he figures there is no big hurry. He sees no immediate need to insure his hereafter or to perpetuate his kind, for he is sure that he will live a long time and have no end of fun of the kind which a church might regard as sinful.

As for marriage, never a man lived who didn't have some wild thoughts of running away before the thing got too complicated, only to discover that a gentle but powerful web had been spun around him, which made escape appear to be caddish and dishonorable.

Warn your son against early marriage, explaining that he is the quarry who mistakes himself for the hunter. (I might add that at this time he is more interested in the chase than in the chaste.) The odds are against him, since he is a mouse trying to match wits with a hungry kitten. Even if the cunning feline is not in an eating mood, she may play the game indefinitely, or at least until a fatter mouse shows up. If, for example, all the other high school girls are going to the altar, she is likely to feel half naked without a wedding ring, so the most promising boy is elected to buy it for her.

It has been noted that every unattached woman looks at all men and classifies them at first glance as possible fathers of her expected brood. I am certain, however, that the second look is as calculating as that of a gimlet-eyed banker making a loan on a hayfield.

I remember a patient who was leaving my office one afternoon when it started to rain. While we stood at the window watching the drizzle and the folks running into doorways, she grabbed my arm and directed my attention to a youth entering the post office across the street.

Sure, I said, I knew him, and thought he was a very nice chap.

She wanted to know what kind of husband I thought he would make. I ducked that one, and asked whether he had proposed.

"Heavens, no," she said. "I have never even met him, but I kind of like his looks."

Three months later I was congratulating the young man on winning such a charming bride. If he looked slightly confused, it was only because of the speed with which he had captured her. Poor guy. He might have out-run a man-eating tiger, or out-swum a man-eating shark, but he was a sitting duck for that dame. She picked well, however, and they hit it off fine.

There are a lot of things you should warn your son against at this dangerous age. If he acts too chivalrous, tell him his flame's heart won't be broken if he escapes by fair means or even by plain running away. She doesn't expect to bag all the game flushed, and her only reason for aiming at him in the first place was the scarcity of targets.

A swain's love is overpowering, and the object of it is angelic, according to some poets; but the truth is that the female from the very beginning is a more practical individual than the male. She doesn't expect perfection, and will make do with what she can get.

Here, again, recount your boyhood experiences. Tell your son about the girls you knew instead of discussing his current crush, for anything you say against her will only make her seem more desirable to him.

Stress the fact that you loved many chicks who in later life would have bored you silly as hens. Men change almost as fast between fifteen and twenty-five as they did during the first decade of life, and what suits Junior now may be a long way from his ideal of even next month. What is sauce for the gosling may be poison for the gander.

When I was seventeen, I knew a nice girl who had no more romantic appeal for me than the inside of a motorman's glove. We were just good friends, and she was deeply enamored of another guy while I was practically panting for a gal who had her eye on a catch who had more folding money than I.

We used to pour our romantic troubles into each other's sympathetic ear, and whenever there was a project afoot in which one of us was involved, we could count on the other's help without question.

I never dated her or had any desire to hold her hand, and, in looking back, I sometimes wonder whether I realized she was a girl.

The crowd broke up, as all crowds do, and I never saw her again. I never so much as wrote her or received a postcard from her, but I never forgot her, and often wished we were so situated that I could talk over with her things that troubled me.

Her face—the way she walked and wore her hair—are more distinct in my memory today than those of any of the other members of the gang I knew, and I think I would recognize her voice over the phone even after fifty years. I repeat that I regarded her simply as a sympathetic friend, never as a person with whom I was in love.

Years later, two thousand miles away, I met a girl who, on first meeting, reminded me of this early friend in her approach to boy-girl problems. And, after some forty years of marriage, she still reminds me of that other girl, although they looked nothing alike at any time.

At seventeen, I accepted this sympathetic friend as a friend only; at thirty, I appreciated the same qualities so much I married a woman who had them. I can see now that, had I married some other type of woman, I would not have had the happiness that has been mine over the long pull; but if someone had suggested as much to me when I was young and green in judgment, I would have thought he had a hole in his head.

By shifty foot-work and a natural tendency to run, a young and inexperienced man may put off the day, but the heck of it is, he has little chance in selecting his life's partner. That's one argument against early marriages. Another is that at least one of the two parties involved has no idea of the kind of mate he wants.

It's a terrible mistake to marry on the shaky foundation of passion.

"People in love are the worst possible ones to pick mates objectively," said the Reverend Daniel A. Lord, whose formula for a successful marriage is: "The four M's—mind, money, manners and meals."

Jerome K. Jerome made another pertinent observation: "Happy is that couple which can kindle the gentle warmth of affection before the fierce fires of passion burn themselves out."

And they burn out fast, especially in a young buck of sixteen or seventeen.

Son, there will be plenty of time for you to think of marriage after you have been properly educated.

In a few years you may be far less concerned with romance, and much more interested in picking a mate who will wear well.

PART TWO

From Halter to Altar

The female of bachelor is "lady in waiting."
ANONYMOUS

7

Pursue learning, don't learn pursuing

One of the benefits of a college education is to show the boy its little avail.
RALPH WALDO EMERSON

Between eighteen and twenty-five the average young man completes his education and gets married. Both jobs require a lot of hard work and money.

The wise parent makes his son finance at least part of his education, for it is natural for one to appreciate more what he pays for. Your son while in college may envy boys with convertibles and dolls to ride in them, but the study of female anatomy never helped anyone pass an examination in calculus.

"There is a time to embrace and a time to refrain from embracing," said Solomon. Girls are fine, but only as a recreation at this stage. Be moderate, son, or else girls, like shooting crap and playing pool, will take up too much of your time and will cost you money. With any kind of luck you'll have at least forty years to conduct serious research on women, and there will be plenty of specimens about when you are ready for the noose.

Spend too much on fun while in school and your allowances won't stretch from one payday to the next, and you'll find yourself in hock to money-lenders. The habit of living just a bit beyond your income is harder to break than the cigarette habit.

One of my sons loved money for the sake of seeing how much fun he could squeeze out of it, and it troubled my drop of Scottish blood. When he was ready to go to college, I researched his probable expenses for the four years and deposited the entire amount to his credit in a Salt Lake City bank. Then I told him that was all there was going to be. If he wished, he could have a toot for one year, or go through four years in comfort.

The bank gave him a letter of credit to the eastern bank near the university and, unknown to any of us, requested the bank to keep the Salt Lake City institution posted on his financial progress. A year later this institution informed me that the young gentleman was conducting a loan business with other students, receiving much higher rates of interest than banks could. If he wasn't picked up for usury, said the report, he would probably own the university in time.

My son stretched that bank account over four years of college and had enough money left to finance his Master's Degree. Meanwhile, his mother was worrying about her poor boy living in a garret and eating hotdogs to stay alive. He has never asked me for a dime since he was eighteen.

If you can, choose the largest college that will accept you, especially if you plan to enter a profession. True, many of our big industrialists graduated from small colleges, if they happened to get past high school, but they started farther back than they would have if they had a big name school behind them. (In some cases, the extra track gave them more momentum.) A man may be the biggest ass since Balaam's donkey, but it's better to be a runty one from a good big university than an average ass from a school of less standing. For one thing, it will take longer to recognize your inadequacies. I have seen graduates of colleges of metallurgy put in charge of smelting operations over men who helped make the first converters, and, so help me, some of them had to be led around by the hand to keep them from falling into the blast furnaces —but they had a big name college behind them.

Try to get a well-rounded education before you specialize. A man educated along just one line may be a nut in all others. Most of us have a limited brain capacity, and if we fill the void with only one line of thought, there is less room left for what we loosely classify as common sense. It's a good idea for a specialist lacking a rounded education to bridle his tongue and not pop off on any subject outside his field, even if the stars foreordained him to be a genius along some line.

But whatever profession you follow, skip some engagements and hang around law courts until you get the hang of courtroom procedures. It will not only help a lot if ever you have to face your wife's attorney, but it may sometime prevent you from making more of a fool of yourself than the script called for. There is absolutely nothing so comic, yet so pitiful, as a pompous, egotistical physician squirming around in the witness stand at the mercy of a sarcastic little attorney armed with a few out-dated facts on the relationship between weather and bunions. I know, because much of my professional life was spent in close relationship with the legal side of medicine from an industrial standpoint.

I knew many lawyers, and learned early that the answer they most hate and fear, when trying to discredit a professional witness, is a simple "I don't know."

The jury don't know either, and this gives them a feeling of kinship with the witness. Thus what he does say they will believe, now that they know he is honest. This also sours them on the attorney, because they are pretty sure he has just familiarized himself on one trick question and knows nothing more about the subject. When a jury has a bond of understanding and sympathy with the witness and begins to try the attorney in its own minds, it's time for strong men to flee the courtroom.

There was one doctor in Salt Lake City who was the scourge of every attorney in industrial practice. He didn't know too much and, aware of his limitations, was not afraid to acknowledge his ignorance. But he had an honest face and a simple, direct manner of speaking. When he took the stand for the opposition, the wise old owls sent in the budding Clarence Darrows to cope with him, and then sat back and enjoyed themselves, even if it cost their clients money.

Never pretend to knowledge you don't have while in the witness chair. It's no fun to be scalped by a lawyer in front of a bored audience that is looking for someone to laugh at.

Now you are in college. At the beginning of the semester, look over the professors with a calculating eye. You are drawn to the kindly soul or to the easy-going lecturer, but any wisdom you absorb will be forgotten the next day if that is your criterion. Don't do it. Pick out the worst double-dyed s.o.b. on the faculty. Sharpen your brain on a grindstone, even though you don't enjoy the process. You will learn more in his classes because you don't dare to come in unprepared, and what that man pounds into your skull will remain there.

I had one professor who followed Osler's teaching methods, which, briefly, were to damn the patient and his welfare, make a diagnosis, then sit back and watch nature's wonders.

All through his courses in physical diagnosis I soothed my tortured soul with the idea that once I had my diploma I would knock his nose back where his ears ought to be. But

There is nothing so comic, yet so pitiful, as a pompous physician squirming around on the witness stand.

later, when the water began to get deep, I could see his ugly face staring at me across the patient, as if daring me to miss one little symptom or physical finding.

By the end of your second year in college you have a better idea of what your mission in life will be, and you may start specializing in your third year with that goal in mind. In any case, it's about time you started to evaluate your potential and try to match your desires with your abilities. It is time, as St. Paul counseled, to "Put away childish things" and to ponder, like St. Peter, "What manner of person ye ought to be?"

So far you have been learning the rules of nature. You are a pile of the sands of experience, and are foreordained to build some kind of structure. Will it be a shack with every timber out of plumb, or a sturdy edifice within which you can dwell in comfort for the rest of your life?

Study your heredity so you will have a better understanding of the moods, tensions and latent abilities within yourself. You must draw a plan and assemble all your building materials to see if you can build the structure you want. You are the sum total of your inheritance. Therefore you should draw an inventory of your dominant and recessive characteristics. The result can be compared to a good herd book such as is used to keep the blood lines of bulls, horses and dogs. If you are a Mormon, this will be easy, for it is a part of Mormon religion to keep the best possible records regarding the ancestors of every living member of the church.

Otherwise you will have to dig for the information, but you will probably find some maiden aunt who will gladly impart reams on the subject. However, she is likely to romance it a bit, and when you sum it up you may conclude you are a mixture of Socrates, Marco Polo and George Washington. You will be lucky if you get much dope beyond the second or third generation, but accurate pictures of them will help because they, too, are the sum total of their ancestors. It's interesting to find out how many of them were residents of local jails and how many were hanged, but such information is incidental to the family picture.

What you most want to know is their occupations, tastes in reading, leadership shown, and the willingness to accept community responsibilities. Also important is their body structure, prowess in sports, their health and longevity, what diseases they had, their habits in regard to alcohol, and their after-dark activities. Finally, what rang down the curtain on their lives?

Don't worry if parts of the puzzle don't mesh. Some time in the dim past a neighbor's bull may have busted out of the pasture and left his mark on your herd. Certain abilities and characteristics, on the other hand, may lie dormant for a generation or two before again manifesting themselves. Even in animals, wherein man is more careful about blood lines and breeding, a red and white calf may be born into a well-established Holstein herd of black and white cattle. And there are runts in other families besides pigs.

If there were many alcoholics, guard yourself in the use of alcohol. If they were a sickly breed who died early, your insurance company would be happy to have the information and raise your rates accordingly.

Were they students or laborers? Your natural bent is something you will have to struggle against. My own family tree was somewhat cluttered with teachers, preachers, missionaries and politicians. I started out with the ambition to reverse the trend and began my adult endeavors as a railroad man, but look where I wound up.

If you set down on paper the data you gather about distant ancestors and study the trends and predispositions buried deep within you, you won't be so surprised if they take over.

You can combat them if you are prepared to recognize the symptoms.

If you want to be a financial giant, pick a tramp for a father. Looking at it the other way, if your Dad was loaded with coin of the realm, your chances of ending on skid row are brighter. Incidentally, because of the natural animosity of the young adult male toward the leader of the herd, you have probably so far fashioned your life as much at variance as possible from the paternal pattern, even if you still live in the same house with your Pop. Your father may try to dominate your life, but if you have any guts you will tell him to jump in the lake. You, and you alone, have to live your life.

You must analyze your parents and the way you were guided in your early years, for that, too, has a bearing on what you are to be.

Was yours a happy home, with all things within reason provided for your physical and mental welfare? If so, your chances of setting the world on fire are pretty slim. But, you say, that was the way I advised them to bring you up, and now I am suggesting it is wrong.

Don't expect me to follow one line of reasoning clear to the end without considering other possible outcomes. A doctor who doesn't hedge a bit in giving a diagnosis will find himself going one way, his patients another.

There is nothing positive in medicine except the unexpected, and there are no statements made about it that cannot be proved wrong.

A doctor and a friend were riding in the country one day when the friend called attention to some white cattle on a hillside. He remarked on the beautiful white color of their hides. The doctor said they seemed to be white on this side, but he would reserve judgment about the other side until he saw it.

What I said is that if a boy was raised in a good home where law was respected and family relations were pleasant, there would be no reason to worry about that boy getting into too much trouble.

It is also true, however, that said boy will be pretty well satisfied with the life he knows, and will see no reason for straining himself to get ahead. A kite, remember, rises against the wind. Only by accident will such a lad achieve his potential, for if he is to go very far, he must be tempered by fire. There must be many blows on the anvil before he takes the shape of greatness.

If he never had an empty belly, he doesn't know the satisfaction of having a bag of beans stored in the cellar, or of a safety deposit box that contains a few war bonds.

So write up your parents in your private herd book, expressing your opinions of them at the moment. In future years, you may find some changes and discover that the old man was not the nut you supposed.

Each of our two sons grew up firmly believing that the other was the fair-haired lad who got all the breaks. After they had been away awhile, both agreed that things looked different from a more mature angle.

You'll have no trouble cataloguing your parents. You have been psychoanalyzing them since early childhood, else you would have suffered more lickings than you did. You'll discover later that their natures will explain many peculiarities in your own progeny, for parents are merely the hosts of the cells that form your body and brain. You, too, are the connecting link between your parents and your offspring.

Sex glands and cells which were part of you when you were born lie dormant until you fuse them with those of your wife. Your bodily makeup may resemble one or both of your parents, but more often will be a fusion of both strains. Your brain is such a collection of inherited characteristics that you can tune and play it like a violin, provided, of course, the occupants of your family tree weren't all dolts.

The blueprint you make for your guidance *must* be down on paper, and it should never be seen by any eyes but yours. We need visual as well as mental impressions to fix things in our minds.

Now is the time to look yourself over most carefully, examining your physical and mental endowments. If you are big-boned and heavily muscled, with a hard head and not much in it, your future may lie in professional body-bruising sports. If not so well endowed physically, pick a course where you can make your head do most of the work, always supposing that there is something in it.

One pre-air-conditioned summer day I was assisting a professor in a gall bladder operation on a large fat woman, and was leaning over her chest a bit. The professor turned to me. "If they ever invent a way to do abdominal surgery sitting down," he said, "you'll be good." Having reached the same conclusion long before, I later spent a good deal of my professional life sitting on an office chair or on a bedside stool waiting for some woman to produce a citizen. And I happen to know that everyone else present in that Missouri operating room has been dead for years, while I can still stand erect for the time required to play "The Star Spangled Banner." The person who said, "Never stand when you can sit; never sit when you can lie down," had a point.

Be cruel and frank with yourself, even if it hurts your pride, and don't get too discouraged with the picture. And if it is too promising, you have forgotten one prominent ancestor. His name was Ananias.

Your notebook is not just the vagrant thoughts of an adolescent mind, but a living thing that will grow with you. And think of your satisfaction should you turn out better than your early estimate!

Like any other romantic literature, your notebook will be flat without girls. Describe your ideal wife. You'll never get her, but neither will you be satisfied with her opposite. Think about the home you hope to provide for her. My dream was of a blue-eyed blonde in a yellow brick house with a big porch across the front, and Dorothy Perkins roses climbing over everything.

I got a red brick house with practically no porch, a brown-haired wife and mildewed roses—but at least my wife had blue eyes.

Put down all your secret longings; they may be of value once you have grown old and have retired, as we shall see.

A couple of years ago you wanted a hot-rod and a pretty girl beside you on the front seat. Now you may want a Cadillac with a mink-coated siren. Well, before you invest in a Cadillac, a mink coat or a siren, pause to read the second chapter of Ecclesiastes. The guy who wrote that was probably the greatest success, from a dollar and siren standpoint, who ever lived.

King Solomon cornered most of the world's gold, owned all the livestock and was acknowledged to be the No. 1 sage. He also cornered the market in women, and those he didn't take time off to marry he kept on a piece-work arrangement.

Everything that pleased him he took, and he seemed to be able to keep peace among all these women. He must have been good when we realize that such a doll as the Queen of Sheba not only had to come to him, but had to pay her way in with presents when she arrived. And that gal wasn't looking for wisdom.

Solomon even had his own band to lead the parade whenever he chose. In fact, he was all of the things that Hitler, Stalin and some of our own dear departed merely dreamed about.

And after Sol got all this, what were his conclusions?

"Vanity, all is vanity." In other words, all the satisfactions expected from being able to make a bigger show than the Joneses next door proved empty.

"To make a man happy, add not to his possessions," said Seneca, "but subtract from his desires."

Put your notebook in a safety deposit vault and consult it from time to time when the need arises. Remember that the historical part will be of value to your own sons when they reach the time when they, too, have to build their own house within themselves.

I have given this "herd book" idea clinical trials, and it works. Of course, some of those old child-guidance biddies or a half-baked psychiatrist might say it would tend to make a boy too self-conscious, or that making such an inventory might upset his already overburdened brain. He might even contract ulcers.

Well, son, if you were born to have ulcers, now is a good time to find out so you can avoid playing the stock market in the future. You must be forearmed for the struggle ahead of you.

And you must learn as early as possible that if you don't have the fire-power to take Omaha Beach in your personal world war, you must pick out a less defended stronghold to assault.

8

Go slow when you a-wooing go

A man admires the woman who makes him think, but he keeps away from her; he likes the woman who makes him laugh, loves the girl who hurts him, and marries the woman who flatters him.

Anonymous

Now is the time to catch our free-running young stallion, break him to harness and teach him how to do the world's work. There is nothing that so fills us with nostalgia, when we get old and frayed, as the sight of young males running free without a care in the world.

As we take leave of the careless and carefree young of the preceding pages, I am reminded of an incident of my early years of medical practice.

My territory covered an area about the size of Connecticut, and although most of my patients lived within a radius of ten miles, a few hardy souls clung to the little watering holes out on the great American desert. They were ranchers, stock men and a few miners. They had to be cared for, and sometimes this involved a round-trip of a couple of hundred miles over poor roads in barren country mainly inhabited by rabbits, coyotes and bands of wild horses.

On one trip, the alkali dust got into the wooden wheels of my 1920 horseless carriage, and the spokes became loose. I made it to the north end of Granite mountain by wedging them with parts of a knife blade. When I reached this spot, I removed the worst wheel, and, damming a tiny rivulet that came down the mountain, made a puddle in which I soaked the wheel.

It meant camping out all night in this forsaken region, but I was prepared for it and glad of a chance to spend a few hours in the manner of my Indian friends. Besides, it meant that my assistant had to work at home while I had an unscheduled holiday.

I parked my car on a knoll some two hundred yards from a water hole. An hour before dusk some wild horses came within view. They were shy because of the strange object on the hill, but also very thirsty, so after some delay they came down to drink. All but one. He was a two- or three-year-old stallion, dark gray and beautiful compared to the other specimens in the band.

I had spotted him when they were quite far off. He was prancing about the herd, but at a little distance from them. Whenever he got too close, the old stallion leader charged him, ears flapped back and teeth bared, the very personification of fury. The youngster would dance away, then follow his Pa back when the old man returned to his harem.

This brash youngster took a good look at the car, then came in fast, drank his fill and performed all kinds of kid stunts, showing the mares and fillies how brave he was and how passé and over-cautious his senior was. And, with it all, how terribly anxious he was to assume leadership of the herd.

He made a pretty picture against the backdrop of a setting sun that painted the hills beautiful shades of purple. This youngster, so full of energy, grace and devilment, was the ultimate expression of youthful masculinity. Too good looking and daring for his own good, he was a challenge to man's sense of possession.

I wasn't much of a prophet, but I could foretell his future. Some wily Indian buck or white sheepherder would spot him sooner or later and he would spend the rest of his life dragging a broken-down wagonful of lazy Indians over these same hills in search of pine nuts. Or he might become the saddle pony of some equally lazy sheepherder. Either way he'd never see a barn or shed, or taste hay or oats.

There was a third possibility. Some Indian, maybe more hungry than tired, might pick him off with a gun, in which case he would wind up as strips of "jerkee" hanging on a barbed-wire fence to dry for winter meat.

Our hero might come to similar ends, or he might be lucky enough to be captured by a more humane individual.

I have seen all these things happen: the colt, sheared of his masculinity, harnessed to a filly much less favored by her Creator; or saddled and bridled and ridden by an overbearing female; or wasted on a battlefield in a cause that settled nothing; or trotting alongside an understanding mare who pulled more than her share of the load.

Many trails lead from this water hole, but none of us—perhaps fortunately—is given the power to see over the next rise beyond which may be green pastures and still waters, desolate rocks and sagebrush or cactus, or an Indian hiding in a gully with a gun.

But, like the wild horses, we must travel, and now it is time to think about slipping the hymeneal halter over our young man's head.

Married men you know fall into various categories. Some

dwell in happy homes with a wife who, like Longfellow's Indian, "bends him yet obeys him; who leads him yet she follows." (One half-breed Indian squaw I knew was a little literal in this connection; she tried to bend her buck's head with a Dutch oven lid.)

Then there is the couple with two or three children and no money, and father is struggling to get an education. The years have left few marks on his appearance or personality, but his wife shows the strain of raising kids, keeping his passions satisfied and working at something to help out the budget. He is as young and gay as ever, and as susceptible to other women's charms. If he is an interne or medical student, he is probably slipping off with some student nurse every time he gets the chance. I have known such fellows. A boy with a man's job, he is to be pitied as well as blamed, but it adds up to a rough deal for the girl he promised to love and honor.

Another chap has a wife who seemed perfect a few years ago, but now, he thinks, she has tobogganed. She is probably the same woman she always was, but the boy has changed into a man, and they no longer have much in common besides the wedding certificate.

Divorce may be the only remedy for some of these situations, but as I have said, when there are children parents should be made to live together in wedlock as long as the children require the security of a home. The one who breaks the contract should be thrown into jail and left there a while to meditate on his sins.

There are other kinds of marriages and other types of mates. There is one dame who will scare you away from the altar faster than a shotgun can bring you there, but some men succumb even to this scary breed. You visit a friend and meet a wife who *knows* she's a lot smarter than her spouse, and she is most willing to remind him of that fact in the presence of strangers. She interrupts his stories, corrects his English, slanders his ancestry and contradicts every other statement he makes. Brother, don't jump off the dock if you are married to the likes of her. Push her off instead.

In the ideal marriage, husband and wife, while remaining individuals, have learned a skill which seems forever beyond nations—the art of compromise. Respect your wife's rights as a human being, behave like a gentleman with her at all times and see that most of the compromises are in your favor, and you will have a successful marriage.

All this may still be ahead of you, but when you do a-wooing go, take it easy, and consider the customer's wishes.

Are you the kind of man who will attract the girl you want? Like a manufacturer, you must study her preferences in men, as well as in candy, corsages, lipstick and face creams.

Like you, she has passions that are satisfied by family relations, but, unlike you, sexual satisfaction is not her primary goal.

In all nature, the continuation and advancement of the breed depends on the selectivity of the female in choosing the sire of her offspring. All advances Homo sap ever makes result from this up-breeding instinct. Even though the gals have much reason to be discouraged, Mother Nature makes them look at you and wonder just what kind of father you will make.

Circumstance and ignorance may color her judgment, and she is always prepared to compromise her desires to the available supply, but your girl friend has the same desires as the lady deer or the jungle savage woman. Sometimes it's hard to understand what women find so attractive in certain men.

A mining engineer who worked for Anaconda in South America told me of a new man who came down from the States. The new employee had lost his front teeth and had replaced them with a gold bridge that caused some comment. One day the tribal chief called on this man and said the women of his tribe had decided, after talking it over, that they wanted some children with gold teeth. Would the engineer accommodate them?

Gold teeth may not have much bearing on your girl's choice, but your curly hair may be a factor, particularly if she has invested a small fortune in trying to curl her own. One thing that will count, however, is your personality.

From many years of listening to women recount their husbands' defects, I think their greatest gripe is having a namby-pamby spouse. I don't know how many times I've heard an anguished female say, "Oh, if he would only beat me when I get bitchy, but, damn him, all he says is, 'Yes, dear.'" Don't take too much advantage of your wife, however, if she feels this way. Most women have bitchy spells; if your wife does, don't beat her. Just give her the impression you will if she doesn't pipe down.

In *The Alabaster Box*, James Lane Allen tells of several women who were discussing husbands. One said that when she was married her mate told her the story about family relations among deer herds. He remarked that when the buck lost his horns in the spring, the does drove him out of the herd, but once the horns grew in again he became the lord and master.

"I do not intend, at any time," this husband continued, "to shed my horns; I do not expect to use them but they are there just in case."

I admit that I have known women whose preference was for men with no more backbone than a pole-bean vine. All I can say is that some women are born missionaries and can't do anything about it. Most women aren't looking for a Simon Legree, either, but they prefer one to a Casper Milquetoast.

When I was a kid we had a neighbor whose only contribution to his household was coming home stoned on Saturday nights and beating up his poor, hard-working wife.

When my gentle mother suggested that she divorce this

"Oh, Mrs. Peck, you don't know what loving ways he has when he's sober."

monster, she always said: "Oh, Mrs. Peck, you don't know what loving ways he has when he's sober!"

This just goes to show that anyone who writes about human nature has to knock down his arguments every few pages and finally admit to the reader: "I zink maybe I don't know."

What a woman primarily wants, if she has any brains, is a man who will provide a safe and comfortable nest in which to raise her brood. She wants her dreamboat to be clean, but not a meticulous dresser, and maybe a husband who bores her only half the time after they have been married for thirty years.

As for the qualifications of a good husband, it matters little if I have omitted some. Once you are hitched, son, your wife will be glad to point them out to you, listing all the virtues of the man she could have married—a man who, in a moment of insanity, she gave up for you.

9

Oh, what will the harvest be?

Men are generally more careful of the breed of their horses and dogs than of their children.

WILLIAM PENN

Now I hope that you are properly confused as to what a woman wants in a man. Good practice, because the longer you know women the more confused you will become, and you might as well get used to this early.

When it comes to advising anyone how to pick a good, loving wife, most doctors follow Shakespeare, preferring to teach twenty than to be one of the twenty who follow their teaching.

They say that if a person hopes to achieve fame, he must have a law named after him. Here is the Peck Law: Marriage is a feast where the *hors d'oeuvres* are usually better than the dinner.

As Francis Bacon said, "A man finds himself seven years older the day after his marriage."

Earlier I told how young men got into trouble when the

young ladies they were chasing caught up with them. More mature men get into trouble, too, because they choose the wrong qualities in their wives.

I have known women who bordered on perfection in some respects, but I certainly would not have wanted to marry any of them. For example, the gift of compassion and willingness to help others is often possessed by women who will not necessarily make good wives. I knew one beautiful girl of eighteen who married a man twenty years her senior who was a helpless cripple. She wanted security, but she also wanted to mother his four little children instead of rearing her own brood. The way she loved those kids, and the way they adored her, was heart-warming, but I don't think she would have been the wife for me.

I also knew a practitioner of the world's oldest profession who closed up shop and nursed an entire mining camp through an influenza epidemic, never getting more than a few hours' sleep at a time for three weeks as she took care of the sick, among whom were those who had advocated driving her out of town.

I don't think I would have wanted to marry her, either, and I am sure you will be satisfied with something less than this kind of perfection. What kind of gal should you marry?

Why not re-read that inventory you made in your herd book a few years ago and compare my list of qualifications with yours?

You stressed appearance. Well, the most beautiful flowers often fade the fastest, and your ideal, well-upholstered, curvaceous little blonde will likely, by the time she is forty, spread out like a bale of hay after the retaining wires are cut. A French poet, jilted by a mademoiselle, consoled himself by sending her a bunch of roses with this note: "These roses will wither, and so will you."

Just remember that it is farther from forty to seventy than from twenty to forty, though it may not seem so long. And each year, weighted with the burden of doleful domesticity, will seem much longer than it is. When Einstein was asked to define in simple terms his theory of relativity, he said:

"If you sat on a hot stove, five minutes would seem like an hour, but if you sat next to your girl friend, an hour would seem like five minutes."

If you are the type attracted by such superficial things as a nice pair of blue eyes or a shapely figure, may the good Lord have mercy on you, and may none of your children wish they had been miscarriages.

If you take marriage seriously, discount all the moonlight and roses and "love-forever-true" stuff. You are entering the most sacred and important partnership of your entire life. It can be heaven on earth, whether in palace or trailer, or it can be hell on wheels, even if you wangle a wealthy wife. I think it was Michelet who said, "If you wish to ruin yourself, marry a rich wife." And if Michelet didn't say this, Joe Peck does.

Don't rush. The right girl is loafing around some place, and I don't mean at a soda fountain. Your job is to recognize her when you find her. Nature will assist you in the hunt, for, after all, she is more interested in this union than you are.

You only have to live with your wife for forty years or so, but the traits you two will hand down will go on and on for generations, and will have a direct bearing on the destiny of mankind. Size up the stock she came from, since, like you, she will be a blend of her ancestors. If you don't like her folks, you may have a hard time liking your own kids, because half of their chromosomes come from her side of the family.

If I could make one change in contemporary culture, it would be to change the marriage ceremony. Instead of playing the wedding march as the blushing bride advances down the center aisle, I would have all the assembled friends and well-wishers arise and sing that old forgotten hymn, "Oh, What Will the Harvest Be?"

The bride has probably already considered this problem, but she is a realist who, having compromised her desires, has taken the best available father for her brood. But unless the bridegroom is abnormal, he has given no more thought to his offspring than a tomcat does.

I know it is ridiculous to expect a man in love to take any advice in the matter, but I hope he reads this book before he falls too deeply in love. It is a doctor's duty, if nobody else's, to think about what the harvest will be.

If you knew a fraction of the ills suffered by mankind that are due to indiscriminate matings, you would realize the importance of giving the matter the attention it deserves. If you want the Lord to bless you with healthy offspring, it is better to prevent now rather than try to correct later.

Among common diseases that run in families are allergy, deafness, a tendency toward heart disease, diabetes, migraine, cleft palate, many kinds of mental disease, and tuberculosis in all its forms.

I know farmers who spend a lot of time and money trying to keep dwarfism out of their cattle herds, but who show interest in their children's alliances only when one wants to marry out of the family faith.

I had a wonderful opportunity to study hereditary diseases in my practice. I had case records covering a thousand or so families, and most of them were persons of polygamous ancestry who had lived in the area for two or three generations.

When a defect occurred in the original male line I could trace it down through many families of different mothers. I finally figured I was as good as an insurance company official claimed an older medical friend to be. This old boy, said the insurance executive, could tell how long a baby born in town would live and what disease it would die of if it wasn't run over first by an automobile.

In most respects, I believe that the Mormons are the most enlightened persons on earth, but though I preached my doctrine at every Parent-Teacher Association meeting where I was invited to speak, and wherever else I could find someone to listen to me, not more than half a dozen couples consulted me before marriage about the possibility of inherited disabilities in their offspring.

If only one side of the family has had some of these diseases in its history, the chances are just half as bad as when both sides have had the same weakness. Therefore, study your private herd book again and ask the girl to make one and compare it with yours. There isn't a family in the country that doesn't have some of these taints, but without too much trouble you can find a girl who has inherited weaknesses different from yours.

My whole family suffered from migraine, and how we did suffer! But my wife never had a sick headache in her life, and our children don't know what it is to have a migraine headache. They might have known had I married a woman who was as afflicted as I was.

Incidentally, after you do get married, it will be a boon to your children and grandchildren if you keep a medical record, just as families in my day used to record births and deaths in the family Bible. If you do, your grandson may be warned in time that coronary thrombosis runs in the family, and can do something in time before the first attack hits him on the golf course. I think it might also be good for families to read the Bible together.

You are thinking of marrying her. . . . If she were a man, would you enjoy going on a camping trip with her? Would she carry her share of the wood to the campfire and help clean the fish? Could you sit looking into the fire for an hour after supper without making any effort to be entertaining and be considered neither a boor nor a bore?

Check yourself as well as your prospective bride. While courting her you won't let her light her own cigarette, and you will sit patiently in the parlor while she is upstairs putting the finishing touches on her make-up. You rise and beam when she comes down, although she has kept you waiting for half an hour. After you are hitched, what? Will you be as considerate? Or will you expect her to take all your nagging, mow the lawn, shovel snow and wash the windows on the outside?

Give her a hint beforehand if you intend to come home at night, flop onto a chair, and in the same breath demand your slippers, a drink and the evening paper, and snarl if dinner isn't ready. Even in the happiest marriages, chivalry will wane. "During a long and varied career as a bachelor," said Arnold Bennett, "I have noticed that marriage is usually the death of politeness between a man and a woman."

Show her the real you before she says, "I do." Let her know that you expect her to look like a Powers model on the pittance you give her each week, that you will let her light her own smokes, open her own car door and reach for the biscuits. Also, that when ordering dinner when she insists on a night out, you will disregard her wishes and make her eat beans and drink beer.

But don't promise to break too many of your bad habits that annoy her, and don't drool that you will give up some of your pet pleasures if she asks you to do so before marriage. Why not keep some wampum in reserve for bargaining purposes, since she just might have a few repulsive habits also, such as insisting that you buy her a new brown handbag to match that beige suit you thought you'd surprise her with?

Anyway, any promises you make now may not last after your first fight.

All women will try to make you over into their ideal of a Prince Charming, but if the missionary spirit overpowers your flame before marriage, and she mentions some of the bad habits she intends to uproot once she has you, remember that to be forewarned is to be forearmed.

Pick a gal with grown brothers, if possible. She will be less likely to expect too much and therefore won't be too disappointed in you later.

Have a fight with her while you're a-courtin'. If she kicks you in the shins or bops you on the chin, all is well. Anybody enjoys a good clean fight, but a dame who weeps and wonders how you can be so cruel is poison. Just remember that a woman's tears generate more power than any waterfall. Also, shun the dame who will never forget a wrong and will never be satisfied until she makes you feel like a heel, regardless of who is right.

Does your crush get a little high in a gin mill? Women go overboard worse than men once they pick up men's bad habits, and who wants to come home and have his child inform him that mamma is upstairs sleeping off a binge. You don't want *both* parents of your kids to be souses.

Of course, if you are a pea-vine looking for a pole, tear up my prescription and get yourself a dame who can make a good living. Then you can vacuum the rugs, make the casserole, don an apron and wash the dishes and buy a dust cap that matches the shade of your eyes.

10

Sequel to that wedding trip

The best laid schemes o' mice and men
Gang aft a-gley.
ROBERT BURNS

You recall the pretty picture of the gay, virile, little stallion cavorting in the somber desert, silhouetted against the high lights of the setting sun, nostrils distended and feet hardly touching the ground as he pranced and hammed before the more sober mares and fillies. Rash, brash and full of beans, he was an arresting figure when he romped in the prairie and desert.

But now he trades freedom for the hackamore of engagement, and he prances no more as he trails the rope of responsibility to society. A stallion in work harness has lost most of his glamor, and if he tries to arch his neck or skittishly curvet, he succeeds only in looking foolish. The time has come to run him into the barn and put him to work.

How did he come to such a pass? Browsing around, he had discovered that the hay and oats in the mangers of his married friends was better than the shad-scale and tumbleweeds he had been nibbling. Besides, he wanted his ears scratched, and there was that compelling urge to propagate his kind.

His last hours of freedom may be spent with outlaw mustangs at a bachelor feed, but they know, as does he, that he is wearing a hackamore; and even though they put on a good show, the party is as gay as a funeral.

He may shy and prance for the last time as he is led to the halter, but he bows his head in submission when the harness of domesticity is buckled around him.

His last show of spirit is induced by fright. He welcomes the filly harnessed by his side, but that thing they are dragging along strikes terror in his soul. She quiets him with a gentle rebuke or hits him over the head with the neck-yoke, depending on her disposition, and he settles down to the job of making a double-harness team.

Goodbye, little horse, and may the memories of your free-running days never recur to plague you in afterlife. . . .

A pre-marital trip to an understanding doctor will save you money later and make life more satisfying for you both, for at this time you need instruction more than at any other period in your life.

The first hazard of marriage occurs within a few hours after the wedding ceremony, providing, of course, that no torrid rehearsals have been enacted.

The male wants to prove his masculinity, and the bride expects him to do just that, but in his overanxious state there is liable to be a premature explosion, and they both wish they hadn't come to the party.

They silently blame each other for what happened. The possibility that he is less than perfect in his sexual performance is so repulsive to the man that he refuses to accept the idea, preferring to blame his bed companion for his shortcomings. And sometimes he is right. An aggressive female throws him on the defensive, and his bodily urges concentrate in a subconscious desire to run. He must be the aggressor or he just cannot play the game. To flower as a complete man he must have confidence in his ability to dominate the situation; he must believe that he is the greatest lover since Casanova.

If he loses this feeling, he becomes so neurotic he feels all his other accomplishments are ashes, and he will follow any female who tells him he is wonderful, regardless of consequences or the siren's looks.

Newlyweds are lucky if the initial premature explosion doesn't establish a pattern which may later drive the wife to seek medical advice concerning her marital relationship.

Never a month passed, during my years of practice, but some new bride came blushing into my office to explain that she had been discussing marriage with some of the girls at the bridge club, and had concluded that she was missing something in her marital relations.

She had begged her husband to come and save her the embarrassment, but he absolutely refused to discuss the matter with any man—least of all with a doctor.

After the first few times I heard this story, I was able to carry on from there and save wives the embarrassment of recounting all the painful details.

I found that the old gag about infant impressions being carried over into adult life seemed to satisfy her and at the same time protect the honor of my sex.

I would explain that the husband was still suffering from the first insult to his manhood which happened when the doctor who welcomed him into the world proceeded at once to snip off a bit of his most prized appendage, and from the inborn fear that every doctor was bent on repeating this outrage.

To show the difference between attitudes, I explained the female willingness to undergo the most searching physical examinations, while the male clung to his trousers, like the mythical heroine in a death-before-dishonor drama, when all the doctor wanted to do was examine him for a hernia. I added that such a conversation as the one she had at the bridge table was impossible in a male gathering, since the code made it unthinkable for a man to discuss his private sex life with another man unless it was connected with a joke.

I warned the bride that this condition would last as long as her husband did, or, to be conservative, until he was about sixty-five; and that if she ever showed by her actions that his efforts were not appreciated, she could expect other women to enter his life.

Once she realized that she was dealing with a retarded mentality (from the sexual angle), she was quite receptive to my lecture on the differences in approach to sex inherent in man and woman, and she usually left determined to take her spouse in hand and teach him some of the things a young man should know.

A man's instincts are about the same as those of a bull or a billy goat. He thinks it is his duty to place the seminal fluid in the spot where it will do the most good and then get the hell out of there as quickly as possible.

This may be acceptable procedure in the back seat of a parked car where both parties are expecting to be interrupted by a cop's flashlight, but as bedroom etiquette it is most inadequate, because the lady requires more time for fulfillment than her spouse. One serious little matron, who told me of her efforts to slow up Pop a bit, reported disappointing results. His limit was two hours, she said. *Two hours!* Some women, once they start wrong, never accomplish their desires.

Any good doctor will tell you that the average woman takes longer to achieve a state of sexual readiness than men. Compromise is therefore necessary. The young (or old) husband should develop tricks that will increase his bride's ardor, while the woman should learn to hold him off without hurting his feelings or getting him discouraged.

To avoid embarrassing details, I will again resort to a figure of speech, talking about one thing and meaning another.

Compare a man to a modern car equipped with power steering, quick starts and high speed, but minus brakes and absolutely helpless if the starter fails to work. There is nothing worse than a car that won't start if you want to go any place, and many apparently insignificant things can prevent it from starting.

A woman is more like the old-fashioned Model-T in performance: it is more dependable once it gets going, but what a job to start it on a cold morning! Unlike a modern car, the more you work at it, the more likelihood there is of starting the motor.

For those who never drove one of these mulish machines, let me describe the way to start them. With a little imagination you can transpose the procedure to a successful marital relationship.

Since there was no antifreeze in Model-T days, the last thing a driver did on a cold night was to drain the radiator, and in the morning the first thing he did was fill it with hot water. Then he raised the hood and poured hot water on the manifold and carburetor, jacked up one hind wheel, advanced the gas lever and retarded the spark. He grabbed the choke-wire in his left hand and the crank in his right and began to wind her up. This was a slow and tiresome procedure and it seemed endless; his eyes popped, his breath was gone and his back felt broken, but he decided to give her one more whirl, and if that didn't work, he figured he'd get a horse.

During that last crank the engine exploded with a rattle that sounded like a cement drill, and if he wasn't prepared for it, the crank flew around and knocked him clear across the garage.

A slow warm-up, with particular attention to every detail, and yours will be a happy household with neither party looking over members of the opposite sex with that tell-tale gleam.

But if you are remiss in this duty, you'd better prepare for trouble. Some girls will cheat; others will make the doctor rich. They will get back pains, congested ovaries and acquire a miserable outlook on life.

If so, blame yourself. You remember, in your bachelor days, when you had a lively session with some girl who refused to go beyond a certain point in her love-making. You spent the whole evening with an organ erect and prepared for action, and, if you gave up the struggle and went home, you suffered acutely from a back pain, and your testicles felt as though they were as big as oranges and twice as heavy. When I was a boy, we called this condition "stone-gullions," and it was common with all males. Some found that a trip to a house of sport or self-abuse relieved the condition quickly, while others suffered it out.

In early married life you are apt to desire sexual satisfaction every night. If so, think of the girl—stone-gullions every night and no opportunity for relief! Just imagine how she must feel. No wonder she seems to grow less and less willing to engage in such calisthenics.

Now, perhaps, you may better understand why this definition of a woman was once so common: "A biped with a pain in her back."

Your Creator gave you the equipment, but you were completed first, and He didn't foresee that the second model would undergo changes on the drafting board which would make her so different in her reactions.

Now, if ever, is the time to realize that gentleness and patience are the cardinal virtues and the key to a happy marriage.

PART THREE

From Time Clock to Ticker Tape

A man is young if a lady can make him happy or unhappy. He enters middle age when a lady can make him happy, but can no longer make him unhappy. He is old and gone if a lady can make him neither happy nor unhappy.

MONZ ROSENTHAL

11

Fictitious domination of the male

Marriage is a ceremony in which rings are put on the finger of the lady and through the nose of the gentleman.

HERBERT SPENCER

Heywood Broun was a smart cookie who knew his way around the unfair sex, and he had some good advice to offer young married men to prepare them for the shaping years that fall between the ages of twenty-five and thirty-five.

At this time a man jumps on the treadmill of failure or the ladder of success as he tries to make his way in the world. He is trying to build a marriage career and a business career at the same time, and if he isn't careful he may find he is doing the work of what was supposed to be a double-harness team.

In Heywood Broun's time, men got off to a good start. "It would be interesting," he once said, "to figure out just how many foot-pounds of energy men have saved themselves, since the creation of the world, by keeping up the pretense that a special knack is required for washing dishes and for dusting—and that the knack is wholly feminine."

Take the hint, men, and keep up that pretense.

Your grandpappy and the sires of the family before him were no fools. They perpetuated the rules of behavior that were handed down from ancestors as far back as those who first came down from trees. Though modified through the ages, those rules were inbred.

Then something happened. I have lived through four wars in which our country managed to become entangled, and the sum total of all of them didn't have as much impact on this country as the revolutions in which women concurrently figured. While the men were away, the women made hay.

When man's inventive genius relieved wives of the drudgery of housework by giving them mechanical gadgets, the womenfolk found time hanging heavily on their hands; so, to keep busy, they started sniping at man's traditional position in society—which was in the saddle. With characteristic female guile, they infiltrated rather than battled it out in a fair fight.

Men were so busy killing off their planetary neighbors that they were unaware of this new menace, and before they woke up to the danger their wives were running a lot of things in ways that satisfied neither sex.

Now we are between the sword and the wall. Man, by and large, fills only the jobs that women don't want, and, even at that, often in a subordinate role. How does our once spirited little stallion react to all these domestic changes?

Man became perhaps not a willing but at least a non-resisting serf, just as the stallion did once he was captured and gelded. The results would be ridiculous were they not so tragic.

Of course, I am an old man, so I think the world has been

going to pot ever since Adam's fifty-first birthday. But just consider what happened:

Thirty years ago, divorce was uncommon, desertion was purely a male prerogative, and homosexuality was something we read about in French novels. Today, women collect more divorces than Indians collected scalps; wives run off and leave their husbands to care for the kids; and every hamlet has its queers.

All because the old buck lost his horns. He shies away from dominant women; and some of these women become so masculine in their approach that they attract other women who want to be bossed and whose husbands have failed to exercise that birthright.

Men turn to other men because they cannot have a feeling of mastery in their sexual contacts with women. Having become impotent, they turn to other men of like frustrations because they feel at least equal to them.

I am sure that women are more horrified by what has happened than are men, and they are trying in many ways to retreat from their position of dominance.

Some forty years ago, Dr. Hertzler advanced a hypothesis which young women of today seem bent on proving correct. "The only way to keep a woman happy," he said, "is to keep her barefoot and pregnant." (When I go into a supermarket and see sandaled young matrons with their big toes protruding like snapping turtles' heads, and followed by a troop of children, I wonder whether husbands aren't doing their best to keep women barefoot and pregnant.)

Human nature simply cannot change so rapidly, and women's rights, now that they have them, are not nearly so attractive as women's privileges, which they have largely lost. Women who were too smart to demand their rights, and who retained their prerogatives, laugh at their progressive sisters.

My wife and I spent a recent holiday with our son's family

in Berkeley, California. On Christmas afternoon we followed the time-honored custom of going down to the crossroads to watch people arrive and depart. In grandpa's day, folks watched for the coming of the stagecoach; in my day we gathered at the railroad station when a train was due. On this Christmas day we drove to the International Airport in San Francisco to watch the planes coming and going.

Three lanes of cars, all sardined together, were going in the same direction at a frightening speed. Beside us in the next lane was a big limousine driven by an imposing looking dame whose front elevations reminded me of Mt. McKinley and the Matterhorn, and these twin peaks were merely foothills on the approach to the stern and rocky eminence which served as her face. Beside her sat an older model of the same general design, and in the rear seat were their husbands. A sleeping baby was cradled in the arms of the younger man. The older husband looked as if he had given up the fight long ago, and the most masculine thing about the younger one was one of those little eyebrow moustaches so common in oppressed males.

My daughter-in-law, half turned around in the front seat of our car, was chatting with my wife. My son was driving and I, as is usual when women are gossiping, was asleep with my eyes open.

Suddenly there was a lull in the chatter. My wife and daughter-in-law were staring at the occupants of the big car that had just drawn up beside us. They exchanged smiling glances.

The old bag in the front seat of the limousine caught the whole picture as quickly as I did, and gave us a glance that would wither a cactus plant. Not a word was spoken, but the silence was eloquent. Here in our car were two well-bred women, both competent drivers, who shunned the wheel as long as their mates were available to handle it, and who were frankly amused by others of their sex who seemed to be in such complete command of the situation.

You can recount similar instances. At parties women admire the successful career woman's clothes and tell her how wonderful it must be to be independent. Then they leave her for the company of some housewife and swap methods of dominating males in a womanly way.

You can keep your wife contented, if not happy, without keeping her barefoot and pregnant and without buying her orchids every week, and the time to begin is before the bloom of the honeymoon fades.

It may be a good thing if she has to work after marriage, but be sure it is a womanly occupation and that she doesn't bring home more money than you do. If she works, you should assume some of the housekeeping chores, but there are certain things you must not do.

Carry out the garbage, but don't cook or wash dishes unless she is sick. You may dry the dishes, because in this case you are merely helping. Let her take the lead in such chores.

Clean up the mess you made by dropping ashes and paper on the living room rug, but don't scrub the kitchen floor or make the beds or you will lose face. She will try to saddle her chores on you, and you may be so much in love you can deny her nothing. If so, be so awkward and sloppy that she will grab the dish cloth in disgust and chase you out of the kitchen. If extreme measures are in order, drop a favorite dish on the floor and break it. If she asks you to hang wallpaper, louse up the job and she will never ask you again.

If she insists that you wash the kitchen floor, use a mop and be as slop-happy as you can. And if she asks you to cook meals, make a mess, and I *do* mean mess. If you fry eggs without burning them to the pan, you'll get to fry eggs often. If you have no luck in burning them to a tasteless crisp, you might try sprinkling them with pipe ashes. But whatever you do, don't prove yourself a better cook than your wife. If you do, you'll not only hurt her pride but will be kept at it while she plays golf with the girls, who will marvel at her cleverness in making a sucker out of you. It was a smart husband who first prompted a woman to say: "There's nothing so pathetic as a line of clothes hung up by a man." Thanks to this pioneer, this is one job even a lazy wife never gives her husband.

Buy her new clothes, if you wish, but be warned that she will return them next day and will enjoy bragging to her girl friends about your masculine ineptitude. Your ineptitude may be one of the few things about you that she finds enjoyable.

You may buy jewelry for her, but not a hat.

You can tell her how to vote, but not how to wear her hair.

Expect to be bawled out for leaving things scattered around the bathroom, but don't say a word about the powder that covers the tops of dressers like a mantle of snow. That is, unless you want to go on the trouble standard in a hurry.

You may hint that you like pot roast for dinner, but don't raise a fuss if you get hamburger instead. (She is always in an awful hurry around meal time, and frozen pot roasts aren't yet available.) You may improve her cooking technique by mentioning how much you enjoyed some other woman's pot roast, but just be sure it is one of her girl friends and potential rivals. As far as your mother is concerned, you will be safe if you admit that she never fed you much more than corn-meal mush and turnips.

Don't say her clothes are unbecoming, and if you must remark about some other woman's appearance, be sure her get-up in no way resembles your wife's.

Don't ever let her choose your clothes, although she will think this her inalienable right. Offer to wear the suit she picks out for you, if she wants to argue about it, but only provided she will wear the dresses you choose for her.

I often think that the one thing all husbands should buy,

even if they have to hock something to do so, is a tape-recorder. It is far more useful than a kitchen range. Though the playbacks may at times embarrass you, her decisions of yesterday will keep you from being called a liar when you play them back tomorrow.

Let her furnish the house as she wishes (all decisions recorded), but reserve one little corner of the living room as your own, and fight for your life rather than lose your favorite chair and reading lamp. Every man is entitled to a chair that fits his particular bottom, and if your wife tries to move it, bolt it to the floor.

Use your paycheck for rent and food. If she works, let her use hers as she sees fit—for new clothes, kitchen curtains, beauty aids and parakeets. But restrain her, using force if necessary, if she tries to buy you a tie.

Have separate bank accounts, but insist that she pay as she goes. To her, "charging it" is just like getting it for nothing, but it may mean tears on the first of the month when she finds she has to return the merchandise.

Hard cash is better than a checkbook. She won't part with cash unless she really needs something or runs into a gambling machine. If you ever pass through Nevada, change a five-dollar bill into nickels. At the first stop she will get all the thrills out of the nickel one-arm bandits that would come from the dollar machines, and she can play twenty times as long. It is the pull of the lever that fascinates her rather than the winnings.

My own sex is not averse to taking a chance, but on many visits to Reno and Las Vegas I have often counted the gambling patrons, and they invariably run five women to one man, as far as one-arm bandits are concerned. This is not so true of games such as twenty-one and shooting crap.

Her capriciousness may at times provoke you, but it is the quality you most cherish in her. It gives you a superior feeling, since you consider your every decision so logical and well supported by facts.

Actually, when it gets right down to the busines of living, she has more sense in a minute than you ever will have, but she knows you enjoy being Sir Oracle and sees no harm in allowing her whims to take over now and then just to please your vanity.

Never get sore and cuss her out. She wants to be treated like a dear little girl who doesn't know any better. Scold her, but scold her tenderly.

Remember that custom decrees that women must struggle a bit before they give up anything. Her resistance makes her more desirable, and her surrender is her own form of enjoyment.

Marriage demands a steady hand at the helm, and if you would keep the crew content, act like a captain who knows his business and steer a safe course. You must learn that course yourself, forgetting all the hidden rocks and sand bars your mother told you about. Never let the crew catch you steering by that outdated chart.

Each family must follow a slightly different route to happiness, but if you used any judgment at all in your choosing, you have a shipmate who is willing to take the watch when it's her turn. See that your own contribution is that of the man you hoped to be when you wrote that inventory in your personal record book.

There will be difficulties which we will take up when baby comes. You have enough to do in the next few months getting domesticated and housebroken.

12

A pregnant wife has a whim of iron

The prospective father will find that his wife will want apricots only when the apricot market is at a dead low because of a seasonal lack of supply.

JOHN GOULD

You have not been found wanting during your nuptial flight, and your bride thinks you're a wonderful guy who is ever anxious and willing to demonstrate deep affection. She had taken it for granted that you would give her a little time to get over the romance, but your honeymoon didn't quite conform to the blueprint, and, like the queen bee, she came home slightly pregnant. This was nature's purpose in sending you off on a get-acquainted (or get-reacquainted) journey, but nature and brides don't always agree on details.

Your wife hoped and expected that you would play this trick on her some time, but it's just too bad to get down to the real business of life with such a bump. Connubial bliss is one thing, but precipitate results are something else. The tree of marriage may be stunted if it bears fruit before it attains proper root development and growth.

The baby will prove that, like the bull and billy goat, you are a male able to beget your own kind, but over the years you have wasted thousands of these little pollywogs around the countryside, and the fact that one of them finally hit the target doesn't mean your marksmanship is anything to brag about. It may, however, get you into trouble with your sweet bride.

Like all pregnant females, she may entertain a violent change of heart toward the cause of her condition, and you may wind up in the dog house before you know your way around the bedroom. She is still just a girl, and mother never told her it would be like this: tossing her hash, and a sense of smell so acute she can't cook beefsteak without feeling like a caged tiger. She will develop an appetite like an ostrich and hanker for the queerest things. In the middle of the night she may insist that you run down town and get her a bottle of beer and some hot pastrami, and she will say, "You men never understand," if you dare tell her the stores are closed. Don't be too surprised if she tells you to buy a baked pickle or to make her some ice cream made out of fresh cherries. That is, if cherries are not in season.

Meanwhile, she is suffering acutely, and she knows just who is to blame. It won't do you any good to reason that it was she who took your simple show of affection in earnest; but if you're a typical male, you accept none of the responsibility, figuring it's her hard luck that she finds herself a little pregnant.

Poor Pop! Although you are about to become the luckiest man in the world, you are not exactly bubbling over with joy at the prospect.

You hold the emesis basin for her while she screeches that if she had ever dreamed things would be like this, the whole

In the middle of the night she may insist that you run downtown and get her a bottle of beer and some hot pastrami.

damn race could die out for all she cared. This is the time for you to lean on any acting talent you have, because, other than feeling a bit sorry for her, you actually have little interest in the matter.

If you pity yourself, go to the zoo and look at the king of beasts crouched in one corner of the cage while his pregnant mate prowls, growling and snapping and, as like as not, making a pass at him now and then. Your troubles aren't unique.

You may remark to a friend that your wife is now more even-tempered than ever—she is mad all the time. If you add that she is pregnant, your goose is cooked good and brown. Your friend tells his wife, she tells her pals, and of course they are so solicitous they simply can't wait to phone your missus to offer crocodile words of sympathy. At just about this point your sweet wife will blow her top; so when you sneak in the side door, prepare to duck, because things may be flying in your direction. By this time, being unusually perceptive, you realize that you'd be better off if you had told your friend that your wife wore feed bags for panties instead of mentioning the calamity that has befallen her.

I don't know why women long so for pregnancy, why they seem so proud of it in later months when they look like a black snake that has swallowed a rabbit, or why they get so furious if anyone finds out about it during the first few months; but, man, they are touchy on the subject.

Women of her acquaintance who are members of the lodge of motherhood will gladly assume the role of initiating her into that ancient and hallowed institution.

The ritual doesn't vary much. Each member of the lodge thinks up all possible complications, then the women meet and assign one horror story to each flannel-mouth so there will be no duplications, and then send one to call each day and try her best to scare the wits out of the prospective mother. That's the way it seems, anyway. Along with their tall stories they cite the taboos so dear to the heart of woman. The pregnant wife must not clean a chicken or look at a two-headed horse. It might mark the baby. If you abuse a man's privilege of being ugly, they advise against her looking at you any more than necessary. Otherwise the baby might look like you.

A lot of women nurse the fear that what they do during pregnancy will have an adverse effect on their children, which explains why they look more harried than usual. Some think that the personality of their unborn child will be directly affected by any emotional experiences that are unsettling, but this is more flapdoodle. Women worry enough without having a flock of gossipy old crones coming in with their old wives' tales.

Let your bride suffer, Pop. She'll have her fun later when she joins the lodge and meets other bewildered brides. The truth is, however, that having a baby under present-day conditions is as likely to have serious consequences as falling out of bed. Even in my day, we didn't lose more than one mother per thousand births. But you know how much fun it is to see the poor blind candidate ride the goat, and the girls must have fun, too.

You and your wife will get through this terrible period somehow.

If you are not yet convinced that you are an unfeeling dog, she will remedy that when the big time arrives. Console yourself with the thought that if you hadn't initiated this train of events, she would have had you down to a doctor's office by this time to have your semen examined to see if you had short-changed her. Just keep your horns on, even though they must be in the velvet stage for a time.

The ordeal passes, and she gets to the point where the front of her gown twitches as if she were hiding kittens under it; she becomes the sweetest thing this side of heaven, and probably the prettiest, too. The old masters had good reason to paint pregnant women, knowing that no other beauty had such a radiance. An old hag is likely to have the face of an angel at this time.

Now her days are as radiant as her complexion, and the parties and showers begin. The dump is cluttered with pink and blue things, all too small and fancy for anything but a four-pound girl. There are enough tiny hair brushes to outfit a maternity ward, and all are pink. Of course the odds are that the kid will be a boy and as bald as an egg.

Watch where you sit these days; there is sewing scattered all over the place, with needles just waiting to jab your fanny.

You better cut down expenses and save money. Babies haven't changed much over the centuries, and the stork is still the bird with the big bill. Production costs have skyrocketed.

In my early practice, doctor, nurse and housemaid seldom set the husband back more than fifty dollars, and you probably didn't cost over seventy-five when you were launched, but this is going to be a full color, wide-screen production.

As the deadline nears, you sleep with your sox on and with your pants draped over the bedside chair as if you were a fire laddie. Every night you fill the car with gas and back it into the garage, instead of driving in as usual, so that not a minute will be lost when you have to race the long-billed bird.

When the moment arrives, you will probably have a flat tire or a neighbor's car will be parked in front of your driveway, locked with the brake set. Some night, right in the middle of a beautiful dream in which you are breaking a hundred for eighteen holes for the first time, she taps you on the shoulder and says she has a pain.

You frantically phone the doc and a sleepy voice answers. "Oh, doctor, she has a pain!" Your voice quavers with honest emotion.

But the unfeeling doc has a "so-what" attitude.

You always thought this stinker was not the doctor for your

little chickadee, and now you curse yourself for not holding out for a younger man, who would, you are sure, have come galloping. Your doc between yawns tells you to time her pains and let him know in the morning how far apart they are.

So you walk the floor, watch in hand, as intent as a bookmaker clocking a new nag on an early morning workout.

Your wife drops off to sleep, and as the minutes drag you are sure she has forgotten a pain, so you wake her and inform her that the next pain was due thirty seconds ago—something must be terribly wrong. The poor tired kid mumbles something that sounds like, "Oh, go to hell," goes back to sleep, and leaves you with your worries.

Being a prospective father is an awful thing, with a lot of prenatal cares, but most fathers live unscarred through the ordeal, though I did have one faint and fall on the side of a stove, causing a scalp laceration that required stitching before I could concentrate on the main event.

Eventually you get her to the hospital and are firmly advised by the sour-pussed old supervisor to go get lost. You collapse on to a chair in the waiting room, swearing never to go through this harrowing experience again. By now you are convinced that the medical profession doesn't know a damn thing about prenatal care for fathers.

Pick out a chair with a good view of the hall so you can exchange smiles with the pretty nurses flitting past looking so sweet and desirable in their clean white uniforms. A guy has to have something to think about to keep from going nuts, and as he engages in a little innocent flirting, he is surprised how often the nurse has to pass the door on her rounds after she catches his admiring glance.

You are missing a lot of fun connected with this wondrous occasion. When you were born it was more of a hand-work procedure, with little of the impersonal assembly line technique that takes all the romance and interest out of creating anything.

But some day, when a movie queen gets caught and has her papoose at home, some medical authority will rave about the difference in mental impressions of a home-born baby. The baby is an individual instead of one of those assembly-line products shelled out like peas in a cannery. Soon all the gals will decide to have their babies in the old-fashioned way.

In the beginning, doctors had little to do with the birth process, and, because they generally are naturally lazy, they brought some women to hospitals where it was easier to care for them. Since little was known about infection at that time, many mothers died from germs brought in on the doctor's hands. In my day, it was considered better to keep mother at home because she was immune to her own germs, and doctor and nurse wore sterilized rubber gloves. Then came antibiotics, and doctors no longer feared infection, so back to the hospital went mother, thus saving the doc long hours of bedside vigil. All this costs more, and sometimes they check you out with the wrong baby. As to the baby's impressions, I cannot say, never having pursued that line of investigation because of my deficiency in baby talk.

There is nothing so funny in medicine as watching the birth pains of the man who caused it all.

In my day, all the ladies in the block were determined that the father should not be allowed to miss the arrival of his first born; so, he was present, and a more useless piece of baggage was never conceived. If he had any use at all, it was for comic relief.

You could depend on him for nothing. Once I asked a Papa to hold a coal-oil lamp. When things got a little messy he fainted and dropped the lamp on the feather bed. The mother about-to-be popped out of bed like a singed cat (and looked somewhat like one in her short delivery gown) and sped across the snow-covered lawn to the next house. We threw the bed out the window and rushed next door where the job was completed on the kitchen table.

Often in the old days Pop sat at the head of the bed where his wife could maul him when having a pain and curse him when she wasn't.

When the child came, he looked on it with horror. Had Adam been around when Cain and Abel were born, he most likely would have thrown them into the creek and have said nothing about it. Then where would we have been?

Father's first words, usually in a muted whisper, were, "Oh, Doc, do you think he's all right?"

On being assured that the head, which at the moment looked like a pineapple squashed in transit, would assume a normal shape in a few hours, he was somewhat relieved, but then he got all excited, wanting to do something to show the new arrival that he was welcome.

I remember one doting father who thought the little stranger should have some form of nourishment, and when I told him to fry the baby an egg, I'll be damned if he wasn't back in five minutes with the worst burned egg I've ever seen, expecting me to feed it to the baby. If Papa sheds tears and hugs his wife as he exclaims about the dear, beautiful new baby, set him down as a blasted hypocrite—a man who will neglect his family and his doctor bill.

If his shoulders droop with the weight of added responsibility and his smooth brow is creased with worry lines, you are witnessing the real miracle of birth: the metamorphosis of a boy into a man.

But some fathers I knew never faced up to their responsibility. Once, when I was summoned to a modest home in Utah to deliver a baby, I ran into a father who obviously didn't believe in being forehanded. Thanks to him, it was one of the weirdest deliveries I ever made.

It was winter, with lots of snow on the ground when I arrived at dusk after a forty-mile drive, and the stork was already circling for a landing.

I jerked out my instruments and sterilizer and rushed to the kitchen to boil up. The fire was out, and when the father rebuilt it, it wouldn't burn. He guessed the pipe was clogged, he said, remembering that his wife had been complaining about it for the past month. I gave the pipe an impatient whack with a poker and the whole damn thing collapsed, leaving soot thicker than Los Angeles smog over everything.

Just about then he remembered he had forgotten to get fuel for the Coleman gas lamp, so he struck off cross country to borrow some. By this time it was dark, and the wife was yelling that the stork had arrived. I rushed into the bedroom covered with grime, threw back the covers and groped around in the dark trying to find the baby. I finally located him, and wherever I touched him, my fingerprints were outlined with coal dust.

Mom hadn't laid out anything to dress either herself or the baby, so I fumbled around in the dark until I found something soft in which to wrap the child, since it was as cold as a snob's greeting to a backwoods cousin. I discovered later that the swaddling clouts were my white silk muffler. It was the only confinement case I ever performed with the help of the Braille system, accompanied by a few choice cuss words.

When the father returned and we got a light going, I was too disgusted to laugh when I looked at the babe. Of all the wretched looking brats, he took the cake. In the first place, he had landed on an old blanket, and a lot of the fuzz stuck to him, giving him a coat like a mallard duck's after the outer feathers are plucked. On top of that, I had smeared soot all over him. The only clean thing about the child was the inside of his mouth, and had he been crying when I found him, I suppose I would have dabbed that up, too.

By the time we cleaned the chimney and lit the fire, the nurse arrived. I left after quietly informing the father that if I never saw him again it would be too soon.

I was so dirty and black when I came home that the dog, not recognizing me, ran under the bed.

Such cases were exceptional. Most prospective mothers were good housekeepers and, as if forewarned of the stork's coming, spent the last day or so before the launching cleaning up their houses from cellar to attic. We called this the nesting instinct and asked them to advise us when they showed a burst of energy so we could get ready to greet the stork.

To Mom, of course, the new arrival is always a thing of beauty. "Doctor, isn't it a lovely baby?" she invariably says. The best way to handle this emergency is for the doc to shake his head admiringly and say, "Now there *is* a baby!" That covers everything.

My enjoyment of poor Pop's predicament was ghoulish, I admit, for, like all male physicians, I hated the convention that forced me to be present at this feminine rite. But to retain the family's business, we had to deliver babies, and I might say that Grandma, as well as Pop, often gave us a bad time.

One of my older colleagues had a case in which the labor had been difficult. He sewed up some lacerations and warned the mother to stay in bed until he could determine whether the stitches would hold.

"Nonsense," her mother-in-law said, "I always get up the second day and get my husband's breakfast."

The old doctor peered over his glasses. "That's funny," he said to her. "I didn't know cows went to bed at all."

Your first experience as a father won't seem funny, but in your excitement you may do peculiar things. One gink ran three blocks in bare feet through snow to get the doctor when his first child was born; but when the second came, he got up, shaved, dressed leisurely, and had a cup of coffee before taking his wife to the hospital.

Incidentally, take the rubber sheet from the crib along when you head for the hospital with mother. Babies have been born in automobiles and the only thing harmed was the car upholstery.

13 *It's cheaper to move than to pay rent*

There is no place more delightful than one's own fireside.

CICERO

Birds build nests before they lay their eggs. If you and your new family have no nest of your own, live with your wife's folks instead of yours.

Your bride will fight with her mother, but she has been doing that since she was old enough to squall. A simple little scrap with *your* mother, on the other hand, could be disastrous.

You will hear both sides of any arguments your wife has with your mother and will need the wisdom of Solomon or Dorothy Dix to keep out of it. At this stage remember that into the closed mouth the fly does not get, and that no argument really gets hot until a peacemaker steps in.

You may despise her mother, but you don't have to be with her all day, whereas there is little escape for your wife if she is in your mother's house. Under such circumstances, your mother would show her inherent feline nature.

If you refuse to live with in-laws, it will be cheaper to rent for the first few months instead of buying a home, one of life's major investments. You may have insufficient funds to purchase a house and furnish it properly. Besides, if you rush into buying a dream castle, you are quite likely to be taken for a ride.

You will be told that it's just like buying a car: a down payment and twenty years (instead of the one or two years for a car) to meet future installments. You have had experience in buying a car, but real estate is a bit out of your line, so pick your realtor with care. As in other professions—mine included—there are potential robbers and confidence men listed in the phone book. There are also sharpies who know how to get around the law.

Avoid high-pressure salesmen. The man who sold me my little farm in California drove me out there. "Well, there it is," he said. He retired to the shade of an oak and let the place sell itself.

Look the place over as if you were going to loan money on it instead of living there yourself. Do you like the architecture? Is it comfortable or is it one of those glorified hen coops all plastered over with trinkets the magazines call "aids to gracious living"? Roadside motels offer everything in the way of gracious living. If that's what you want, buy a tourist trap.

If you like outdoor living, pick out a place that will give you that in January. There are other considerations. In southern California flies are so bad that outdoor food looks as if it were garnished with raisins, and only bears enjoy the outdoor evenings around San Francisco and our central valleys and foothills, where sweaters are a must when the sun goes down.

Frills? Swimming pools are wonderful to pose beside, but after the first month you have to lick the kids to drive them in.

Children, being more forthright, consider them little more than oversized bathtubs, and shun them accordingly. In some neighborhoods, however, if you don't have these extras you are as conspicuous as an old Ford alongside a new Cadillac.

When you find a house that is tailored to your wife's dreams, examine the neighborhood. Count the kids and dogs visible at any time, multiply by five and add ten more for visitors who will arrive for a ball game in front of your house, with first base on your new lawn.

Check the area to windward for rubbish heaps, garbage dumps, reduction works and smog patterns. Check the time it took you to drive out to the place. That, multiplied by four, will about equal the time it will take you traveling to and from town during rush hours.

Examine the soil either by digging a hole or looking at some excavation. I know of one big building project near me that is built on hardpan. You have to hire a big digger to bore through it to plant a tree.

If the community has no sewer system, expect nothing but trouble from septic tank drainage. Modern homes with dishwashers, automatic laundries and such, require half an acre to absorb the waste from each dwelling, and if you don't have that much land you may find your neighbors' sewage seeping through your front lawn. This adds little to outdoor living. Remember, too, that when the sewers come, the tax rate will rocket.

Look on all wells with suspicion, for water in them may well mean septic tank drainage from the neighboring lot, which means that water will be full of colon bacilli.

Have an electrician check the wiring. You can't run an electric kitchen on the usual small wire used in a home.

Pull the bushes away from the foundation and look for termite tunnels running up the cement. If the property is new, try the texture of the foundation with a pocketknife. Down close to the dirt the cement will crumble a bit if they have skimped on the mix. Crawl under the house and examine the inside. They may have plastered the outside surface with a stronger mix than that used in the main foundation. Prod the sills and girders with your knife to see if termites have been at work. Termites can ruin your investment quickly, and it costs plenty to get rid of them.

Pound the paint job a bit in a place where it won't show to see if it flakes off, and cast a critical eye on the roof. Check joints and gutters for leaks. Crawl up into the attic, and, when your eyes get adjusted to the dark, look for tiny holes where light filters through. When it rains, each little hole will be a Niagara. Any roof except copper or slate will probably need to be replaced ten years after its laying.

Inspect the living space. Are there cracks in the plaster above the doors? Do the windows move easily and can you shake them with your hand? If so, the wind will do an even better job and keep you awake with rattles and bangs. Cracks also make earthquakes seem more terrifying. My advice to oldsters is don't retire to an earthquake belt.

Has there ever been a fire in the fireplace? If not, burn something and you may find out that it is a useless decoration. I once owned a house in which the fireplace flue was lined with wood. Fortunately, it was in Utah where there was no wood to waste on such poor heating arrangements, and so there was a gas log installed in it. A circulating type of furnace will give you as much heat as a stove, and it looks just as cute as the little bear den that adorns most living rooms. If you can get oak to burn, you will cut down your gas and oil bills.

Pound the closet doors with the heel of your hand; some of them are made of orange crate salvage and depend on a coat of paint to keep them from falling apart. Lean on the wall; if it gives under your pressure you can be sure that the house is stuck together with spit and optimism. Go back down cellar and up into the attic and measure the distance between joists and rafters; maybe the building inspector had his vision dimmed with green paper. Examine the furnace. Its capacity will probably be printed on the name plate. Balance this against the BTU's needed to heat this kind of construction in your area. Any heating firm can give you the tables.

Park near the house in the evening and count the insects that fly, sing, or chirp at dusk. They, too, may discourage outdoor living during the evening. If that's the kind of al fresco life you want, why not invest in a tent and a sleeping bag?

Does the next door neighbor practice on his trombone or turn his television set on loud enough to be heard in his outdoor living room, and does he keep it that way until three o'clock in the morning?

Add forty percent to the purchase price to cover new furnishings. No set of curtains was ever suitable for two houses, and the living room furniture that was so attractive in one spodunk may look just awful in a new location. Changing doors and closets and redecorating to make your wife happy will cost another twenty percent.

The interest you will have to pay on your mortgage, hidden in the fine print of the contract, will be more than ten percent of the total cost. New shrubs, sidewalks and paving, draining that old sump under the house and other minor details will add another thirty percent, so you can be sure that a fifteen thousand dollar house will wind up costing you about twice that amount, and will depreciate faster than your automobile.

Six percent of this sum is eighteen hundred dollars. You can rent a pretty nice apartment for a hundred and twenty-five a month and have no lawn to worry about.

If your bride suggests that you build your own house, while she does the interior decorating, you are going through the wringer head first. I built two houses, so I know what I'm talking about. Although every man must travel the same steep road and learn from experience, here are a few hints.

First, pick out the plan she wants above all others and order twenty copies of the blueprints. Hide one and give her the rest to mark up. She will spend the next three months happily changing them, and her final effort will look nothing like the original print. When she finally gets tired of this make-believe, send her home to her Mom for a long visit. Stuff her plans in the fireplace, dig out the original, and go to work.

You'll find that everything needed in the construction has doubled in price since the first estimate, and the carpenter's union won't let you drive a single nail, which is just as well, maybe. Also, that every tiny change which you try to incorporate according to your wife's wishes will add a thousand to the cost.

Therefore, don't let her come back, if possible, until the paint is dry. If she is pregnant, tell her that the smell of paint will nauseate her.

She will probably think that everything about the place is wrong. The entrance is on the wrong side of the house, so she may insist that your dream castle be jacked up and turned around. You will be called a blithering idiot, and she will always play this record as long as she lives in the monstrosity. But if you move away after a year or two, it becomes the perfect home, and she will weep every time she thinks about having had to leave her dear little house.

Every spring an experienced builder I used to know altered my new home in accordance with my wife's wishes. I finally remarked, when we were adding up the bill, that I reckoned there was nothing about the house left to change except its location.

"Don't kid yourself," he said. "When my wife and I got married I bought a lot right across the street from her home and I told her I wanted to build our house exactly as she wanted it. She spent every day we worked supervising the job.

Well, we moved in and lived there more than fifty years, and she made me change it at least once a year. Today, believe it or not, she hates the damn place and swears she is going to burn it down and have a house that suits her. That's a wife's privilege, brother. You can't win, so just turn your tail to the storm and let the wind blow. The Almighty had to add discontent to women's virtues to keep them from out-classing the angels."

That's one reason husbands should invest in tape-recorders. Record her decisions and play them back to her when she denies that she ever said such a thing in the first place.

Meanwhile, whether you are living with in-laws or in a house you rent or own, you now have a blessed event to contend with. You should have prepared yourself for your role in the unfolding drama by studying the relationship of the sexes as worked out by generations of men who traveled this way before you. Don't ignore their experience. Remember that your forebears, working under much more trying conditions, brought to manhood a lot of sons who stand head and shoulder above modern man in reason, intellect and accomplishments in art, music, government and the science of living. True, man now lives to a riper age, but it would take a Solomon to figure out whether this is a blessing or a curse.

Let's now focus on Papa's problem after the new baby arrives.

14 | *Your children are not your children*

A child is a figure of wax under a modeler's thumb.

ANONYMOUS

A baby doesn't smarten up until he is about six days old. At that time he will take advantage of your weakness and pretend he is fretful merely because he wants you to take him for a midnight stroll in the bedroom.

It's all right for you to take your turn walking your new son at night if he has a legitimate beef, but don't let him disturb your dreams simply because he isn't sleepy. I have seen many a baby quieted in hospital nurseries by the judicious laying on of the nurse's hand in a strategic spot. Don't spoil your son and make him a one-man chamber of horrors.

There are certain duties a man should assume in caring for the new arrival, but there are other things which, if wished on him, will destroy his manliness and make him lose his traditional place in the family circle. Your little boy is an individual with all the good and bad traits of his ancestry, so you'd better start bending that twig right from the beginning.

Don't get up and prepare his meals. Nature provided a source of nourishment for him that does not have to be warmed, measured or purchased; if it isn't available, blame it on your wife's laziness or on some fool doctor's scheme to cause more office visits and thereby sweeten his kitty.

There isn't one woman in ten who couldn't nurse her papoose if she weren't afraid it would make her breasts seem less beautiful, yet nothing a pediatrician can dream up will give that baby such an immunity from disease and as good a start in life as the food nature intended him to have. If your wife wears proper supports and lies down when nursing junior, her breasts will look just as enticing after lactation as before, and probably even more so. Also, her generative organs will return to normal without any expensive fussing by doctors trying to prop the uterus into place.

Don't tell your wife I said this, but there is nothing so conducive to a normal involution of the organs of generation as scrubbing the kitchen floor on hands and knees. The ligaments of the female pelvis were put there with the idea that she would clamber around like a monkey, and while the uterus is heavy and swollen after birth, she had better revert to that mode of travel for a while.

The one who stuffs it in should also carry it out. Once, when a young couple visited us with a new baby, we were sitting around the fireplace gassing about the old home when the baby began to fret. Papa got up, took the baby from his mother and carried him to the bedroom to change him, and his wife never missed a word as she kept gabbing.

My wife looked at me, astonished. We had both known the husband from birth, and his parents before him, and we were reasonably sure that his Pop would have let the bilge accumulate clear up to his neck before he would have changed his boy's diapers. The bride was a stranger, and we both were filled with wonder at her speed and ability in emasculating the son of such a rugged sire. I am sure that my wife thought the intracacies of a safety pin were beyond my masculine understanding; she had seen me remove thousands of them before taking a rectal temperature, but had never once seen me put one back.

Poor little guy, I thought at the time, he has lost his horns before they were out of the velvet, and would forever after be a muley.

Don't accept this chore without a fight, and if vanquished, use guile instead of force. Stick the kid with a pin, pinch him or do anything else to make him scream, and if all else fails, dump the contents of the diaper on the floor and only half clean it up.

It's her baby. The time will come soon enough when he will transfer his allegiance to you, and then it's your turn to take the reins.

Meanwhile, remembering your and your wife's hereditary characteristics, be on the lookout for any troubles that may crop up. You can avoid several things if forewarned by family history. One thing to watch for is allergy. If there is a lot of hay fever, rose colds and asthma in the picture, tell the doctor about them before he injects lockjaw or diphtheria serum or any other compound containing horse serum. Children have died because of neglect of this precaution.

Some persons can't take antibiotics, and there have been deaths from ingestion of a couple of aspirin tablets in sensitive patients.

Watch also for a family weakness in resistance to streptococcus, and if there was much rheumatism or heart disease in your ancestry, watch that kid's throat. Begin examining his throat when he is six months old. Do it when he is well and

I am sure that my wife thought the intricacies of a safety pin were beyond my masculine understanding.

make a game of it, and soon he will open like a steam shovel when you wave a spoon at him. Get the nice pink color of his tonsils and mucous membrane fixed in your mind so that when he gets sick you will immediately recognize the change in color. If the pink in his throat changes to red, slap him into bed and take his rectal temperature, leaving the thermometer in for three minutes. The same applies to his tonsils or that little teat-like structure you know as the soft palate.

A red throat and above-normal temperature in a baby whose forebears suffered from heart trouble means it is time to call a doctor. Keep the kid in bed until he arrives, even if you have to use a club. We have wonderful drugs to cure almost everything except the disease from which you happen to be suffering, but the most wonderful thing in medicine is prevention.

You will meet opposition when junior goes to school, but a perfect attendance record for a child with a family history of rheumatic or coronary condition is a disgrace to his parents.

Discuss this child's inheritance with the doctor, and if the doc isn't interested, get one who is.

If you get nothing out of this book but an interest in your personal herd book and that of your bride, neither you nor I will have wasted our time.

We mentioned that as the male child develops, he turns from his mother to his father. Now it's your responsibility to start molding that little lump into a man.

But don't be overly protective or demand that he follow any prescribed course that you have in mind. Let him get into some trouble on his own, for only women are born with experience. Men have to learn from their sins. And your boy will go higher if he picks his own mountain to climb.

He may look down on your vocation, anyway, preferring something quite different. I would have been glad if one of my boys had selected medicine, but neither ever showed any interest in the profession.

It's your son's life, so let him live it in his own way, with proper guidance, but with no unnecessary interference either before or after he can lick you.

You have reached the age of thirty-five, now. You are by no means at your peak of accomplishment, but you should be well on your way. If you are still punching a time-clock instead of having your name printed on your office door, you have been gold-bricking somewhere along the line. "There are but two ways of rising in the world," said LaBruyère; "either by one's industry or by profiting by the foolishness of others."

Let's hope you chose the first way.

PART FOUR

From Old Age of Youth to Youth of Old Age

Middle age is the time of life when a man looks back and discovers that the mountain he's been climbing is only a molehill.

JOSEPH H. PECK

15

Plenty of room at the top

If you don't appreciate what you've got, get what you appreciate.
GEORGE BERNARD SHAW

The span from thirty-five to fifty-five includes the most productive years of your life, although you have yet to reach the peak of your earning ability.

If, by the end of this period, you have accumulated a fortune, you'll be a few steps ahead of my record. Had I squirreled away that kind of hay, the weak moral fibre which binds my good resolutions would long since have been broken. My fourth or fifth wife would be shedding me, my children would be tramps and at least one of my grandchildren would have been kidnaped and held for ransom. My chief concern in life would be figuring ways to beat the inheritance tax, and, instead of trying to tell you how to get along with your wife and children, I would myself be using the trial and error method while paying back alimony to previous wives.

Although I never collected much folding money, my wife

claims I have shown ability to hang onto what I did get, particularly when she wanted to invest it in non-interest-bearing fur coats.

I was taught when young to lay away a few thousand dollars for my old age. Today the Federal Government discourages such thrift. If, instead of working for fifty years and saving my money, I had lived in a barrel and fished for fun and food until I was sixty-five, then got a job as night watchman in a tombstone factory and paid a couple of hundred dollars into social security from my wages, Uncle Sam would be paying me and my wife about two thousand dollars a year for the rest of our lives. That is about the return I get from my savings.

The first lesson you learn on the way up the mountain is that no matter what kind of work you choose, you will have to call someone "Mister" and say, "Yes, sir," until the time comes when you can cash that first social security check. Your wife will have to butter up your boss, unless you want to be leapfrogged, and there never will be a time in your life when you won't have bosses riding your neck.

You don't like to think about this any more than a wild horse likes to think about the bridle, but if you worry about the bit and bridle you must wear, all you will accomplish is to cover yourself with the foam of frustration.

You may envy other men who seem so free of direction in their work and wish you had gone into some other line where you could be your own boss. There just ain't no such animal.

The farmer, once considered a lucky person, today can't plant a seed or milk a goat without having a few government inspectors looking down his neck to see that he isn't breaking some quota or production law.

If you remain content and don't waste so much time envying others, you will have more time and energy to prepare yourself for advancement to positions of greater responsibility. Of course, this will mean more bosses, heavier burdens and

The farmer today can't plant a seed or milk a goat without having government inspectors looking down his neck.

more persons dedicated to the task of giving you the business; for the higher you climb, the more you show your behind, and there is an awful temptation to kick it.

In one company I worked for, I was often at the plant at noon, and ate in the cafeteria. There were several tables without tablecloths where ordinary employees ate, and one large table covered with damask and bearing a centerpiece of flowers where the white collar men sat. Everybody ate the same meal, and the men at the oilcloth covered board came and left when they pleased. But protocol decreed that the office force wait outside, despite inclement weather, until the plant superintendent arrived, and none left until he arose. My salary made me about number six in line from the summit, but I usually sneaked in with the men and ate as I damn well pleased.

Labor leaders are usually worse tyrants than company bosses once they get in position to wield authority, for they are less used to power. The dumber the cluck, the more protocol is needed to reach his ear. I have worked for several big industrial concerns, and whenever I wanted to see the big boss I just walked in; but when my business was with some lesser light, I usually spent half an hour waiting. In my early days, I was a telegraph operator on a railroad. I quit because of a red-necked trainmaster who thought he was a tin-pot Hitler. I wasn't looking for a boss of that stripe, but he did more than all my ambition to spur me into several years of hard work, study and poverty that I might prepare myself for the practice of medicine, where, I thought, every doctor was supreme on his own dunghill.

And then I learned. As an interne, I found out that one must act the part of an extra in a musical comedy. When the star showed up, he had to drop whatever he was doing and salute the king. When this chief of service made the ward rounds, we joined a procession that reminded me of the entrance of the Mikado in the Gilbert and Sullivan operetta. Some of these inflated old goats were worse than that trainmaster. And so?

And so I went to the sticks where I would be my *own* boss.

There I got a couple of thousand bosses. I was the servant of every Tom, Dick and Jane in town, and at their beck and call for twenty-four hours a day. The rest of the time I had to myself.

This supervision included my social life. They knew more about my children's activities and my dog's social adjustments than I did, but fortunately I loved my two thousand bosses and serving them was a joy and privilege. We got along in a most harmonious manner for thirty years.

I learned early that if I convinced them that their best interests were always my chief concern, they cared little about my personal beliefs and standards. They also knew that I took pride in my work.

Every man wants prestige, but don't be too disappointed if you don't always command respect.

Man wants to be a rugged individualist, too, but he is constantly dogged by the matter of conformity. When man came down from the trees and found he had to join with his fellows for prosperity and safety, he had to surrender personal freedom for the good of the community, and each generation finds this task more demanding and harder to accept.

Sometimes men find that their religion or race is a drawback to advancement in their company. If you do, move before you accumulate too many responsibilities. You can't reform, by yourself, a custom that has been prevalent since society's inception, and kicking and creating discontent among others will do no good. Teach yourself, however, to get along with anyone, regardless of racial, political or religious beliefs. You have your religious convictions and I have mine, and we aren't going to argue about who has the right road map to the happy land, since I have never met a religious man who didn't seem to be on the right track.

In my first years of practice, my closest friends were a Mormon bishop and a Catholic priest, and I was supposed to be a Methodist, and therefore a heathen as far as they were concerned. I did about everything their churches (and mine) considered sinful, but since I was not a hypocrite and lived up to my own standards of morality, they respected my opinions, as I did theirs. I gave their flocks the best medical service I could, and they knew it.

We often met in my office at night to discuss things. I remember some bull sessions on Dr. Cabot's book, *What Men Live By,* of which I had an autographed copy. The bishop borrowed the book, and when he returned it a year later, he said he had been preaching out of it for years without realizing it. It's a good book for the intolerant to read. We three agreed that nobody should ever get into the rut of the Pilgrim Fathers, who, said Mark Twain, "came to America to worship God in their own way and to keep other people from doing the same." If you are humble and tolerant, you may be surprised to find the next guy is more dedicated than you. I knew a Hindu who was more devout than the bishop or the priest.

The only thing you can afford to be conceited about is your modesty, and the only thing you should be intolerant of is intolerance itself.

Restrain your missionary tendencies instead of trying to make people accept your beliefs. Be like the Mormon missionary who was sent East to spread the good word. He returned a week later, although he had intended to remain for two years: "If those sinners back East want to hear the true gospel," he said, "let them come out here where it is preached."

It is, of course, unfortunate that to advance in the business world a man must conform to certain tribal customs. It helps if you are the same color as your colleagues, attend the same church as your boss and vote for the same candidates. Much of the same type of conformity improves your chances in community life. Your car must be of recent vintage, if your neighbors' are; and to show that you are one of them, you should grow ivy on the living room wall of your conventional house, which, of course, has a picture window like all the others, and a television antenna of standard height.

It's also a good idea to dress like the other Babbitts. You may want to get out of this rat race, but remember that it is the guy who is out of step who looks funny to the spectators. If you just must be a lone wolf, live on the desert where your howling won't disturb anyone. There are some things you cannot change, so learn to put up with them.

Maybe you know more about running the business than your boss does, but keep it a secret from him unless he asks you for help. As a blueprint for success, the formulas corporation executives and brethren so generously bequeath to graduating classes on Commencement Day don't work as well as Albert Einstein's formula: "If *A* is success in life, the formula is: *A* equals *X* plus *Y* plus *Z*, *X* being work and *Y* being play." When he was asked what *Z* was, he said: "*Z* is keeping your mouth shut."

There is plenty of room at the top, so don't get discouraged if progress seems slow. Every dog, like every dogma, has its day. Your day may not come until you're sixty-five, but even that is something to look forward to—the time when you can tell them all to kiss your elbow.

A couple of years after we moved to our California farm, I went into a record shop to find the lady behind the counter grinning at me.

"My husband and I were watching you walk up the street a while ago," she said, "and he remarked that you were the first man he ever saw who could strut with a hole in the seat of his pants. I told him I'd ask you why if you ever came in here."

I told her that for forty years I had been waiting for the time when I could wear what I pleased, look as I pleased and do as I pleased, and that the shirttail sticking through my trouser seat was a flag of independence.

"God grant that we will see the day when my husband and I can do likewise," she said.

Half a century ago when I was suffering all possible frustrations, I met a Baptist minister (not in church, I'm sure) who called my attention to a Biblical passage that has been a source of great comfort to me over the years. It's one of the few lines of the New Testament which I can quote, because doctors, as a rule, are more apt to study the Old Testament (if they study the Bible at all). Although Moses and Solomon wrote about what man should do, they spent a lot of time describing man as they found him; and since a doctor's interest is man himself, he wants to know about man's misdeeds as well as about his struggles to attain moral perfection.

I cannot prescribe a better formula for the solution to your problems than the one found in the fourth chapter, eleventh verse, of St. Paul's letter to the Philippians: "For I have learned, in whatsoever state I am, therewith to be content."

I don't think St. Paul had the dictionary definition in mind when he wrote this, because he certainly wasn't satisfied with things in general and was working hard to improve them, but he wasn't going to let this ambition spoil the enjoyment of what had been accomplished.

In the many busy years between the time the preacher directed my attention to that passage and my retirement, I am sure I cured more ulcers with that little quotation than with any drug. Of course, I dressed it up, for the patient wants no direct approach to his problems. He feels that his case is

To show you are one of them, you should grow ivy on your living room wall.

unique and that it requires a special visitation from the archangel before the doctor can understand his particular anatomy. But that line from St. Paul is for everyone.

My interpretation of it is that you should not stir up your ulcer with worry about things around you—fancied wrongs, slights, hard luck and disappointments. You cannot, of course, forget them, but you can balance them somewhat with the fact that you are eating regularly, that you have enough money to buy every anti-acid drug advertised and that your stomach is strong enough to take all this advice I am giving you without your regurgitating.

File away all the kicks in your memory section and make them available when the opportunity presents itself, as it surely will some day. Then spend your time thus saved in trimming your light so you will be ready for the chance, when it does come, to thumb your nose at your fancied tormentors.

If you didn't learn in the college of hard knocks, my deepest sympathy goes out to you. The boy who was protected by his mother from the cruel world during his formative years became the "Mom" boy who couldn't adjust himself in the Army. Those "Mom" boys got into more trouble than most of the rest of the Army put together. In civilian life they are the blokes who drive wives and bosses crazy. They are much more likely to become alcoholics and misfits than their fellows who were not so shielded from life's problems. If Pop didn't take a major part in your rearing, you may find yourself in trouble.

Now a word about that badly bent measuring stick—the Golden Rule.

You, like everyone on earth, feel lonesome, and the more you tear around to shindigs and conventions the more evidence you give of your loneliness. Thus you appreciate every contact with your fellow man, but you must show your desire to be friendly first, for he may be even more shy than you.

I don't refer to the kind of glad-handing and back-slapping that goes on when pork and bean tycoons meet at a convention. That sort of thing makes a man suspicious. He may think you are slapping his back to find a soft spot where you can stick a knife.

A smile and a cheery wave of the hand mean a lot to most folks, and the guy whose face doesn't light up when he gets this message is the south end of a horse going north.

If he gets a kick out of showing you a photo of his jug-eared offspring, you can look at it without having your eyes crossed permanently. Be courteous to all and avoid the awful fate of a snob, even if you encounter a person who looks as if he were weaned on green persimmons. Overlook his scowl and you may see a smile break through the dreary bleakness, and then you will feel rewarded.

As a country doctor and the servant of everyone, I could sit on a pile of railroad ties or in a bunkhouse and talk to section laborers, or I could lounge around the big shot's office; and believe me, I learned more about the human animal from the laborer than I did from the president of the railroad. The laborer was more outgoing, less inhibited, and I must say I preferred his company.

The park around the state capitol building in Sacramento is just a block from petticoat lane, and when I go to the city with my wife on a shopping tour, I make a bee-line for the park and look over the bums lolling on the benches. When I find one sitting alone, I park beside him and pretty soon we are clucking like a couple of hens. I have met retired college presidents and guys just out on parole in this park, and every one of them had something interesting to talk about. My wife always knows where to find me when her money runs out.

This habit paid dividends when I was practicing, because, as I said, everyone likes a doctor who is interested in his welfare. My patients remained loyal to me even when younger and better doctors came into the community, and maybe they were better off at that, since the two things you want to be wary of are old barbers and young doctors.

You patronize the gas station where the attendant greets you by name; you buy papers from the kid who remembers the one you read and has it ready for you when you stop; and you go to the tavern where the barkeep knows just what and how much you want on the rocks.

When we first moved to California we, too, were lonesome, having left a community where even the dogs wagged their tails when we went by, to live among total strangers. Sometimes I went marketing with my wife, and one day I went into a store alone.

"Where's your wife, today?" the checker said. "I hope she isn't sick."

Someone had recognized me as a human being. When that girl moved to another store, the Pecks followed her. We followed her to three supermarkets before she quit and got married.

How will you subject yourself to all of life's regimentation and conformity without losing your identity and self respect? The answer is, work at something you enjoy and have pride in what you accomplish. As old Doc Solomon put it, "There is nothing better for a man than he should eat and drink, and that he should make his soul enjoy good in his labor." He said elsewhere: "There is nothing better than that a man should rejoice in his own works; for that is his portion."

That, to me, means pride of accomplishment.

If you are not proud of your labor, quit it and hunt for a job that will make you proud. The dignity and joy of labor well done balance the scales against boredom and monotony, which have been called "the awful reward of the careful."

Maybe that's what St. Benedict meant when he said, "To work is to pray."

You may have heard about the three men who were shoveling dirt on the side of a road. A passerby asked what they were doing.

"I'm digging a ditch," the first said.

"I'm making a foundation," said the second.

The third laborer was of a different breed. "I'm building a cathedral," he said.

16 *Be moderate . . . but don't miss anything*

Learn to spend a perfectly useless day in a perfectly useless way.

ELEANOR ROOSEVELT

There is just so much paste in the tube, so don't squeeze it out too fast. If you want to hang around for a while, live a little slower, fellow parishioners, and "Let your moderation be known to all men."

You should be moderate in eating, drinking, exercising, romancing, fighting and playing. By the time you are fifty-five you can look forward to many more fruitful and enjoyable years of living if you follow the advice of Aristotle, who said: "It is best to rise from life as from a banquet, neither thirsty nor drunken."

Man is made of the same proteins, fats, minerals and carbohydrates as other animals, but he alone is supposed to be endowed with reason. Perhaps he lost something when he was given this faculty, which took the place of animal instinct, for he is the only creature that knowingly does things to injure his health.

He eats when he is not hungry, drinks when not thirsty, and kills when there is no good reason. Wild animals never kill for sport, and it has been aptly said that Homo sap is the only creature to whom the torture and death of his fellow planetary creatures is amusing in itself.

Man is a mass of contradictions.

With all his native reason and education, he knows less about taking care of his body than a cat does.

A cat won't eat things that might poison it; it chews food carefully; and, even when hungry, it won't eat if it is nervous. It won't eat mice when not hungry. It sleeps relaxed when there is nothing else to do, and never hurries except to protect its skin. Let a cat run and it will never get too fat or too thin. And this cat lives by instinct, while you, poor Homo sap, live by reason.

Who enjoys the world more?

Dogs also have a pretty good time, but they have associated with man for so long they have acquired bad habits, some even showing neurotic tendencies.

Cats and dogs, like men, know less about the intricacies of architecture than spiders, but when it comes to the art of living they make Homo sap seem stupid. They have rhythm in everything they do, and that is precisely where you fall down in your quest for good health.

All animals, including man, have the same kind of glands, with the exception of grass eaters, and their glands function in much the same way.

Your body machinery is wound up to run in a rhythmic manner, but consider how you break the cycle.

Suppose we sit in with that little dispatcher at the base of your brain and watch the traffic pattern it has to handle in one day. Maybe you will then understand how it gets some of its signals crossed and thereby causes you grief.

Your alarm clock wakes you with a start, and you jump out of bed and rush through your toilet while your muscles, which relaxed during the night, are yelling for more oxygen. Your heart speeds up quickly to answer the call. You dress hurriedly and race down to an indigestible breakfast of fried eggs, toast, bacon and strong coffee while you read about the latest murder and John Foster Dulles' most recent flying trip, which you are partly financing.

Your stomach needs blood badly to perform the digestive function, but the blood must be rushed through your kidneys to get rid of the excess caffeine. You race out to your car and away you go. Now your brain is begging for all the spare blood available so it will keep you awake and your reflexes ready for any emergency. Some guy cuts in front of you and you get angry, stirring up emotions which are sure to raise your blood pressure; then a blonde drives up in the next lane and your sex centers cry for more blood. All this time your stomach and kidneys need all the blood supply available to get rid of your breakfast.

And one poor little gland the size of a pea has to sort out all these demands in an effort to keep your bodily functions in balance.

The cat eats its breakfast calmly, washes its face and takes a nap; but you tear around all day, drinking, eating, smoking and getting yourself into a tizzy at the office as you try to clear your desk. Meanwhile, your stomach has not had a chance to digest all the food, and it lies inside you and ferments just as it would in a slop bucket kept at a temperature of ninety-eight, which is the body normal.

By noon you may need an anti-acid to correct the fermentation, and this stimulates the flow of more acid. In an effort to empty itself, your stomach squirts undigested and highly acid food into the bowel, which is not prepared for this emergency, and soon you have a duodenal ulcer. Worry and high tension increase this flow, and you may before long need an expensive operation for a hemorrhage. You are sick with a crippled digestive tract, and all your savings are used to support your family while you convalesce.

For God's sake, slow down! You skim the cream from life only once, so give yourself time to enjoy the process. You simply have to unwind at times, and the stress of living all day in the turmoil of industry makes it all the more necessary for you to have leisure in which to digest your food in a tranquil atmosphere. Rest your nerves and brain as well as your muscular system.

Change the pattern of your living. You can do with a half hour's less sleep, or you can retire a half hour earlier at night, and this will give you time to eat breakfast leisurely. Be ahead of the rush going to town and arrive at your desk with calm nerves while your digestion is progressing at a reasonable pace. At lunch, eat something easily digested, and if you have your big meal at night, take a couple of hours to digest it while reading the paper. If your wife wants to rush you off to a bridge game, tell her to pull in her ears. There is nothing harmful about card playing (or golf) if it doesn't require the kind of tense concentration that will raise your blood pressure; but if they are played in a fiercely competitive manner, such games can be killers.

The older you get, the more attention you should pay to keeping the animal part of you in trim. Avoid a big belly, but if you are overweight, be especially careful to avoid exertions. I have known more doctors who died from deer hunting or duck shooting than from overwork at their profession. Undue excitement over a running buck or a flock of canvasbacks, or a date in a motel with some filly under the name of Mr. and

Mrs. J. Q. Smith will pop many an artery that would have lasted a long time under less stimulating and strenuous circumstances.

Many doctors in this connection have been guilty of using their imagination instead of the cruel facts when filling out the space marked "contributory causes" in death certificates—especially in cases of men who die in the prime of life in a compromising setting.

My first lie in this regard occurred while I was still an ambulance-riding interne. I was called to the office of a prominent physician whom I found dead and dressed—but not for the practice of medicine.

Eat and drink sensibly, park your worries at the office, and in times of stress resort to man's substitute for the tranquilizing pastime of chewing a cud—light your pipe. Cigarettes, which are stimulants, won't give you the desired effect, but no man can hurry into anything while smoking a pipe. The Indians found that out around the council fire.

The older you get, the more that old Chinese proverb applies: "Make haste only when extracting hand from mouth of tiger."

If you decide to change your routine you will, of course, run into trouble with your wife.

When you come home from the office with nerves frayed and start to put on your slippers, your sweet bride will wail that she has been stuck in the house all day and wants a change of scene. Tell her to join a class in tray-painting, rug-hooking or basket-weaving, or ask her why she doesn't form a den of cub scouts. Assure her that you will gladly take her to some shindig Friday or Saturday night, when you can sleep the next morning. And don't feel sorry for her if she whines or sobs. Once your pride and joy got rid of you and the kids after breakfast, she tucked the dirty dishes in the electric washer, poured herself another cup of coffee and either called up a

Your sweet bride will wail that she has been stuck in the house all day.

friend or went next door for a little chat. Maybe a couple of the gals dropped in for a gossip session, and they exchanged salty slander about mutual friends who weren't present. By noon she was through with her housework, so she traipsed down to the supermarket to kill more time buying ready-to-serve food.

And you wonder why women live on and on and get plump while you poor suckers lose your hair, temper, ambition and sex urges.

Again we see how man's inventive genius caught him in a net of his own weaving. Labor-saving devices and modern plumbing and heating arrangements which he dreamed up reduced household drudgery that used to keep housewives busy and out of trouble's way. In 1940 a woman could run her home with a thousandth part of the manual labor which her mother and the hired girl expended in 1900, and this added up to increased leisure, more frequent shopping tours and spicier gossip.

Women, becoming restless, joined clubs in search of culture, and the first thing you knew, you heard about the league of this and the league of that—all in league, it would seem, against poor hard-working husbands.

Look, Pop, start your own revolution if you want to reduce your wife's years of widowhood. Learn to be calm and serene, but please don't expect all doctors who give you this advice to follow it.

There was the physician who used to take his little daughter for a ride every night around the block before he put the car away. One night when he was at a medical convention or with a blonde, the doctor's wife gave the girl her accustomed ride. When they returned she asked her darling daughter whether she enjoyed the spin.

"Yes, Mamma," the girl said, "but where were all the sons of bitches?"

To be happy and healthy, ask yourself, "how would my cat go about this?" Devote some time each day to mental and physical inactivity. Burning the candle at both ends may make a beautiful light, but the candle lasts only half as long.

17 *A pig bought on credit grunts all year*

Credit is nothing but optimism over-extended.

ANY ECONOMIST

If trouble comes to roost in your shack, cherchez la femme or cherchez $$$. During the first half of your marriage, money will account for more of your headaches than will strange women with that come-hither look. I willingly admit that money cannot buy happiness, but, as Orson Welles said, it's nice to have it around so you can choose your own form of misery.

Many financial emergencies would never happen if a little time were spent anticipating them. I have carried a substantial accident insurance policy for fifty years and have never collected a thin dime in claims, but had I been disabled twenty-five years ago by a rolling pin or a rocket ship, the insurance company would have been the one to go to the wailing wall.

A well-insured house seldom burns down accidentally, because a man who thinks enough of his house to insure it properly is awake to fire hazards and guards against them. Things we anticipate and prepare for rarely happen; so if you want a long life, insure it and keep the policy in force.

Now that you have a family, preparedness is more vital than ever. If you come cropper, who will pay for the kids' education? I took out term insurance policies for ten thousand dollars for each of my children when they were babies, the dividends to be paid them when they reached college age, in case I had climbed the golden stair.

Term insurance is the cheapest kind available, even if they raise the rates at what seem to be regular intervals, but it pays for one thing only—your death. Because there are no fancy paragraphs involving your mother-in-law's wooden leg, however, there aren't any extra pickings for the broker, and he won't try to sell you such a policy—unless he is your beneficiary. It's the same thing, on a larger scale, as the little slip you buy at the airport before you take a flight. If you get killed within three days they pay your heirs several thousand dollars, although the policy costs only about two bits per day.

I believe in other kinds of insurance and am, in fact, now living partly on annuities with a little help from interest; but since you are still a relatively young man with many obligations and not much money saved up, you need maximum protection with minimum outlay. When the need disappears, drop the protection. As time passes, you should buy multiple benefit policies and, I hope, live to enjoy the proceeds; but right now insist on the cheapest term insurance rates.

There's another reason for taking this step. People form habits early in life, and those habits stick with them. If you get used to keeping a taut ship, sailing always with safety in mind, you will reach port. If you acquire the habit of putting things off until tomorrow, they won't be done until the day after that.

"By the streets of 'by and by,'" said Cervantes, "one arrives at the house of 'never.'"

Everyone in America, it seems, makes a career of being eternally in debt. It is the way of nations, as well as individuals. That kidney-shaped swimming pool and Cadillac pinch the big boss just as much as your new washer and Ford do you. It appears to be par for the course to owe people, thus your check is spent before you earn it.

I made it a rule when first married never to buy anything on time except a house. Pay as you go and you will play as you go. Just remember that each new kitchen gadget will give your wife as big a kick as getting a whole new electric kitchen at once, so spread out the thrills. Moreover, if you let her know you are saving up for a new dryer, she will be less envious of the woman next door who has a rabbit masquerading as mink around her neck.

It costs a lot less if you learn early that all is vanity, and that most folks spend money they haven't got on things they don't need to impress people they don't like. Solomon learned this too late, but he could afford to be a damn fool. Your generation traded its independence for the symbols of success which mean so little in a man's life when he grows old and sensible. One pleasure which you will never have, as a result, will be to be able to look every other man in the eye and tell him to go to hell.

Don't spoil your kids by buying them things they don't need. If you knew more about human nature, you would never ruin your children by over-indulgence. The truth is that your young sons often envy brethren who have to share their beds with goats, and they would in all likelihood turn out better if they had to wear paper soles in their shoes and if they never owned a car until they could afford one. Give youngsters a chance, and they will go native in a big way. Some of the kids who visit us ask why we don't have a little outhouse behind the cottage. Children, contaminated by the symbols of success, eventually acquire an adult cynicism and hypocrisy.

Other than making a plea for an adequate insurance program, I am not qualified to advise you on financial matters. In my day, doctors and preachers who were too successful financially were considered worth watching unless they had inherited the money. Also, they were expected to stick to their own line; a minister who monkeyed with patients or a doctor who took too active a part in church affairs aroused suspicion.

There was one exception. The Mormons administered a rite to the seriously ill, and as the doctor in attendance I highly appreciated it. They offered prayers at bedside for the sick person, and spoke a kind word for the doctor, too, asking that his hand and mind might be guided to do the Lord's will. I was always glad to have the elders take over, since I knew of one poor sinner in the room who needed Divine assistance.

In community affairs, there are some things that experience taught me. A man has a duty to society second only to the one he owes the children he is grooming for the coming age. Join the service clubs, even though the horse-play connected therewith often seems childish. Accept any call to take part in local government, and perform the duties as though it were your own business. Too frequently this chore is left to crackpots and persons who plan to milk the community without giving much more than chin music in return.

The public mind is most unpredictable, and without some safe and sane islands in this flood, results can be disastrous. Most of the world's troubles were caused by people following the ravings of some paranoiac whose delusions of grandeur finally destroyed both himself and all who followed his mad dreams. The survivors rub their eyes and ask what happened.

As a solid citizen you have two responsibilities—one to your community and the other to your family. And as far as your family is concerned, I remind you to be provident, but not prodigal. But if you do run into debt, try not to run into your creditors.

18

Wives are like old shoes

Forty is the old age of youth; fifty is the youth of old age.

Victor Hugo

When an old plough horse tries cutting coltish capers he usually winds up panting, and the same thing happens to husbands of fifty or so who get mixed up with other women. Just because there's snow on the roof, these vintage Casanovas say, don't think there's no fire in the furnace. This immature attitude explains the saying, "There's no fool like an old fool."

Thirty years ago the highways of the inter-mountain country were desert trails—streaks of dust and gravel landscaped with sagebrush undermined by badgers.

Such was the road between Las Vegas and Salt Lake City in the twenties.

Some thirty miles east of the Nevada city, this road began a gradual ascent, spiraling between hills and through gullies until it reached a broad mesa which stretched off into the eastern horizon, whose contours were often obscured by mirages of lakes and trees.

The mesa, too, was studded with little hills and pocked with depressions, but it was level compared with the rest of the terrain. Once the traveler reached this plane, he was confronted by a dozen roads forking toward the east. The roughest and dustiest was the shortest route to the other side. The others were mostly trails made by the wagons of the sheep herders, and led to no particular place.

At the eastern terminal of the main road was a sign nailed to an old shovel handle wedged upright by a pile of rocks. On the sign was painted the word HILL.

Right at this point, the road turned sharply to the left and began a steep, narrow descent down the face of the cliff. This is called a "dugway" in this region. After squirming and twisting like a tortured worm, it eventually reached the valley of the Virgin River, a couple of thousand feet below.

This wretched stream was just a string of pools separated by sand bars, and patches of small willows covered its banks.

In summer these trees gave a welcome contrast of green to the dull, brown landscape, and the weary traveler might have likened the scene to the one described in the Twenty-third Psalm. The water, at least, was still. If wise, he stopped here to fill his radiator and his water bag, for between him and the Elysian Fields of Utah sagebrush lay the closest facsimile of Hades known to man—the Arizona strip.

I drove that stretch one New Year's eve after a Christmas holiday away from the cold and snow of Utah. The youngsters were sleeping soundly before we passed through San Bernardino, and after a midnight snack in Las Vegas, their mother joined them.

It was, of course, Papa's duty to stay awake and watch over them, so I was alone in my vigil over this long, lonesome road. The car lights feebly pierced the darkness ahead.

After we arrived at the mesa, I soon lost all sense of distance, and every dried-up yucca stalk looked like that old shovel handle. The stars coming up over the horizon seemed to be below the level of the land we traveled, and I imagined that the valley and the poorly marked turn were just ahead of my wheels.

All that I held dear depended on my finding that turn safely, and I had plenty of time to think while I was looking for it.

It was like life, I thought—a long, uneven climb up to the point where a man could take upon himself the responsibilities of rearing a family; then the wide plateau full of badger holes to trip unwary feet, and summits to scale. There were temptations to seek smoother trails less rutted and rocky. There was the possibility of accidents and sudden death. There was the turn and the downward descent to the bank of the River Styx where old Charon was waiting with his boat to ferry us to an unknown destination.

Just as "rosy-fingered dawn tiptoed over the horizon," I found the sign, and, putting the car in low gear, began to dip down into the stillness of the night-shrouded valley. . . .

Let's go back for a moment to the point where man first sets foot on the mesa of fulfillment of his dreams and ambitions. I have tried to erect directional signs on a few of the courses to warn the traveler of some of the obstacles ahead, but there are many more forks from the main trail that beckon—and wind up in a desolation of rocks and sands of disappointment.

And there is one trail that will soon branch off from the straight and narrow and invite him down where the Lorelei sings.

Man's moral code down through the ages has been summed up in the cliché: "When tempted, yield at once; it saves a struggle."

We have skipped to the fifty-mile post.

At about this time man discovers that his mate is becoming less responsive to his demonstrations of affection, and performs her marital duties with about the same enthusiasm she shows when she is washing dishes.

The husband knows that women undergo a great change of life at this time, and is prepared for her mood swings, fits of unprovoked crying, and hot flashes. He is most helpful with his advice.

"Why don't you go down and have the Doc give you a shot?" he says.

But he cannot accept the idea that any female could ever grow tired of his love-making. He thinks his proficiency in this regard is unsurpassed. If he didn't, he would lose all his self-confidence in matters having nothing to do with sex.

Besides, from the moment he is born, he has felt complete only when some woman's arms were entwined about him. His romantic life is still near its peak, so just what is the poor devil going to do?

Since the time of his marriage, he has scarcely looked at another woman with anything more than the friendly interest inherent in all males, and has never dreamed of breaking his marriage vows. But now brutish Nature asserts herself, commanding him to go forth and sow his seed where it will be appreciated.

Every man has to meet this problem, and it is to the glory of the race that so many conquer their impulses and continue down the straight and narrow road that leads to the final turn.

But there are those who, like Judah of old, feel that once they are away attending a convention, one little lapse won't be found out, nor will it hurt anyone. And so, like that noble old shepherd, he is taken for a ride by some Tamar, the old sheep-shearer's daughter-in-law who posed as a harlot and gave birth to his twins. Every man of this age should read the story of Judah and Tamar in Genesis. Judah stepped forth and acknowledged his transgressions, which moves most of us to repeat after Kipling, "You're a better man than I am, Gunga Din."

Predatory females seem to know within the minute when old John is most susceptible to their charms, and they lose no time in displaying them.

It may all begin with some giddy little creature who would not for the world think of having an affair with him. She is merely trying out her technique, sharpening her claws like a cat does with a mouse when she isn't hungry.

She straightens out his tie, even if she has to yank it out of line to do so, and brushes an imaginary speck of dust from his collar. Later she tells a friend at the water-cooler that she has the boss's blood pressure on the rise.

His wife once would have told him that his tie was not two-blocked, or would have told him to brush himself off, but, being otherwise preoccupied, she has forgotten these personal touches.

Then along comes a dame whose chances of getting a mink coat legitimately are fading fast. She picks up the scent and begins stalking the old goat. This, like many other feminine procedures, is done in reverse—by revealing instead of concealing.

Pretty soon he is barreling down a strange trail, fearful of the precipices that may lurk beyond the next turn, but unable to check his speed, since his brakes aren't nearly so powerful as his engine.

Every doctor gets involved in these husband-wife wrangles. Mrs. Jones comes in and says old John has gone off his rocker, and she wants the doc to check his sanity. He is stepping out with some little chick after dark, and it's the doc's business to stop it. It's the same old story all the way down the line, with few interesting details to make it entertaining.

Being a man first and a doctor afterward, I would inquire about her marital relations. Does she try as hard as she once did to satisfy his needs?

She shrugs and reminds us that we saw her through the "change" years ago, and naturally she isn't the passionate creature she once was. If you know your patient, now is the time to pound the desk and ask why she didn't put the marriage contract on a term basis if she intended to void it when she was forty-eight or fifty.

This separates the girls from the women. Either she tears out of your office determined to win her man back, or she bursts into tears and calls all men brutes, you included.

You can find no fault with that statement, but advise her that love and happiness are like liberty—you can't take them for granted.

Of course, there are some understanding dames who have their own little ways of bringing heels to heel, and some of the methods I've seen used are dillies. One is based on the assumption that while a man has a predilection for making an ass of himself, he hates to have others know about it. Ridicule is a potent weapon for dealing with men from the age of five to eighty.

One gal came into my office and told me she knew her husband was fooling around with another woman, and she feared he was about to confess his transgressions to her. She had changed the subject several times when he brought the matter up, but she felt it should be talked out.

I advised her to throw him off balance. He would expect tears, thrown dishes and recriminations, and probably pictured himself with his head in her lap while he promised to sin no more, as they do in the movies. I also assured her that if he did make any promises, he would keep them for a week at the most, so the forgiving wasn't worth the results.

I learned the sequel from the errant husband years later when we were discussing another guy's gay-catting.

"Well," he said, "my wife cured me once when I got out of the home pasture. I felt it only fair to confess my sins to her, and she looked at me in a funny way and began to cry. I tried to tell her how sorry I was, whereupon she said she wasn't crying because I had been unfaithful, but because I had found it necessary to take up with such a hideous old bag. It galled her, she said, that her once handsome husband had become so shop-worn that only the cheapest kind of dame would look at him. She even suggested that I come to see you and get some of those new sex hormones; they might check the loss of my hair and make me more desirable. She looked me over every time I left the house, suggesting things I might do to improve my appearance. And, damn it all, I knew all the time that she was laughing at me. I have never looked at another woman since with romantic interest, and I never will. It sure hurts to know somebody thinks you're funny, particularly when that somebody is your own wife."

Some wives know that hubby will soon be left behind in the fast company into which he has wandered, and that he will be glad to sneak back into his chimney corner where he is surrounded by familiar household gods.

I hope for your own self-esteem that when you come to this enticing turnoff from your trail across the mesa that you will have enough strength of character to stay on the track. But if you *should* slip, don't confess it to your wife or anyone else. It sounds too much like bragging and makes you a heel as well as a sinner.

If you do take a wrong fork, may your wife be an understanding woman who will slap you down to size with actions rather than words; and if drastic measures are in order, may she get out and fight for her man, tooth and claw. May she be one of the kind who throw things, pull hair or use any other violent means to best their rivals.

And may the Almighty deliver you from one of those weepy dames who are secretly glad to get rid of you, as long as you keep turning in the paycheck.

Never forget that old wives are like old shoes. New ones look attractive in the store window, but think how they will make your feet hurt, and how comfortable the old brogans feel once you get them back on again.

PART FIVE

The Youth of Old Age

Childhood itself is scarcely more lovely than a cheerful, kindly, sunshiny old age.

MRS. L. M. CHILD

19

At full of tide

The best is yet to be,
The last of life, for which the first was made.
ROBERT BROWNING

Professional athletes have shot their bolt by their early thirties, as have the best poets (with major exceptions like Robert Frost); but most folks don't slip into high gear until much later in life. They do their most important work from their mid-fifties until their mid-sixties, when they reach the peak of their accomplishment and earning power.

When a man reaches the top, the possibility of some day having to relinquish his position of authority clouds over his joys of fulfillment. As a result, he is likely to do some strange things, both of a business and sexual nature.

He may make a wild, unwise investment in the hope of a big clean-up, and the direction his sex drives sometimes take would be funny were they not so downright tragic.

Being a man, I will try to find some excuse for his actions, but I won't subscribe to the theory of a male menopause taking place anywhere but in his head.

In all nature, the approach of fall seems to stimulate the ripening of the seeds or fruit; pumpkin vines that have spent nice summer days just wandering about the garden suddenly settle down and produce little pumpkins like mad. It is the nature of every living creature to secure a sort of immortality by ripening all the seeds possible in the short time before the frost, that they may sprout again in the spring and carry on life's cycle.

This urgency also occurs in women, and the baby born when the mother is in her early forties, when all the other children are about grown, is evidence of this natural drive. I was one of these unfortunate late babies, and so spent a lonely childhood, denied the comradeship of brothers and sisters, which the older children enjoyed.

As we have seen, the male, too, is subject to this natural urge, and is apt to be frisky at fifty. We can't blame all his romantic excursions on an indifferent wife, and we can expect some entertaining antics by this aging pumpkin vine when he gets to be in his mid-fifties.

Somewhere along the line he convinced himself that he was related to the chameleon, and if only he could associate with younger people he would absorb their coloring. His paunch and his thinning hair don't seem to discourage this conviction, and he therefore presents a laughable picture to his fellow parishioners. He reminds you of an aged, sway-backed plough horse trying to gambol over the fields with a bunch of colts.

Other urges are mixed up with all this vanity; he knows there is more possibility of his getting a young woman big with child than he could his wife, and although he has no desire whatsoever for more children, or for paternity suits, he must nevertheless once more show the world that he is a virile old rooster who can crow. This is not true of all men in the youth of old age, of course, but it applies to more than you think.

I recall one gay old grass widower who came in for a premarital examination. He said again and again that he was just as good a man as ever. But he came back from his honeymoon not carrying his shield, but on it. Lumbago had knocked all romance out of his head, and he confided to me that he wished Mother was around. His young bride had no idea how to fix his pillows or turn him over in bed.

All these old goats have an excuse for cutting their sexual didoes which may sound logical to them, but which are ridiculous to others.

Early in my practice in Mormon settlements I was quite interested in polygamy, but not from the damnation status given it by other religious groups.

Going West for the first time, I shared a train seat with a woman from Salt Lake City and asked her about this peculiar custom. The woman explained that Gentiles (non-Mormons) chased girls whenever they thought there was a chance to escape detection, while Mormons married them and treated them all like wives.

At one time or another I talked to lots of old gentlemen who had been blessed with from two to half a dozen wives, and they all claimed that their multiple marriages were necessary, despite the inconvenience of having so many mothers-in-law. More wives were needed to help mother with the work, they said. Since they could not hire female help, they did it just for her. Somehow I never could understand why the original wives didn't seem more grateful for this husbandly solicitude. In fact, I once met one who took strong measures to avoid this assistance, thus proving that you can never tell how some women will react to a thing that seems perfectly logical to their mates.

I remember this instance from my early days of practice in

southern Utah. I was boarding with an old couple, he a rawboned Englishman over six feet tall, his wife a sparrow-type who weighed less than a hundred pounds. There were men living in the vicinity who had two or three wives, but they were not working at it, because the Mormon Church had decided it was unlawful. The kids in these families called each other "cousin." I had never heard about any cousins in this home, so one night while the old lady was preparing supper I sat down in the kitchen and had a chat with her. Being subtle and diplomatic, I asked where her husband kept his other wives.

The woman, who was slicing ham with a long, sharp butcher knife, paused in mid-stroke and glared at me. The twinkle finally came back into her eyes, so I restrained my impulse to run. Wiping the knife on a dish towel, she held it up like a blackboard pointer and said: "That subject hasn't been mentioned in this house for forty years. One night when I was cutting ham, as I was just doing, my husband came into the kitchen and said he had been talking with church officials, and they had agreed that he should take another wife to help poor little me with the work. He allowed he would build another house on the other side of the yard and look around for some likely young woman to fill it. I walked right up to him, brandished this knife in his face and said, 'Abe, you just try it.' "

Should any females read this book, here's a tip: if the old man needs a little violence, don't wave a gun or threaten to pistol-whip him, as I have seen some wives do. He knows you are not familiar with firearms and are not likely to do much damage if you should find the trigger by accident. But if you brandish a knife and show you are familiar with your weapon, he will get out fast. Just a razor knick will drive all thoughts of other women out of his head, and he will rush off to the doctor for a transfusion.

He confided to me that he wished Mother was around.
His young bride had no idea how to fix his pillows.

By the time you are fifty-five there are more important things than love-starved maidens for you to think about. But before going into that, I must give the back of my hand to magazine and television pundits who would make you believe that Ponce de Leon's search for eternal youth paid off. I refer to the sex hormones that were discovered some years ago. All the widely read magazines of the day discussed them, and many of my elderly patients demanded hormones.

One tottering fellow who had married a much younger woman had been tried and found wanting, and he was desperate. He had to have some male sex hormones, he told me, and if I wouldn't give him some, someone else would. I knew they were worthless for the purpose, but every honest doctor will admit there are times when he borrows tricks from quacks.

I gave him a diet that would have choked a goat, a course of exercises that would have made a prizefighter rebel, and some hypodermic injections of boiled water deep in his hip muscles through a large, dull needle. All this hocus-pocus worked the desired miracle, and he was loud in his praise of the wonders of science, thinking the hormones did the trick.

Another case involved a woman, and therefore a much more canny individual. When she came in with a list of the classical symptoms she had read about in a woman's magazine, I had to use the real article, a female hormone, and pray that it would at least do her no harm. At the time this valuable drug was obtained from the urine of pregnant mares, and the Lilly Company sent the profession a nicely illustrated booklet showing all the steps in its manufacture, including pictures of mares standing around with rubber buckets tastefully dangling under their tails.

The booklet was on my desk the day she came in. It was opened—and not by accident—to the picture of the horse. I gave her plenty of time to look at it while I prepared the hypo, and was not surprised when she asked what they were doing to the poor horse.

When I finished explaining, she was bug-eyed with disgust.

"Do you mean to tell me I'm paying you five dollars just to have ten drops of boiled-down horse urine [she didn't call it that] shot into my fanny?"

That, roughly speaking, was the case, I said, whereupon she hoisted her panties.

"Well, that's the last time I fall for such stuff," she said. "Hereafter when I feel the urge I'll get an old tomato can and go out into the barnyard and scoop up the undiluted article and drink what I feel is a good dose."

She is still living, and healthy as a bear, so I guess she survived that trying time of a woman's life just as well as those who had to be treated with the processed hormone. I am also reasonably sure that she never resorted to the cruder method of therapy.

There are lots of ways to skin a cat and the doctor has to know most of them. We deal exclusively with people, some of them the most credulous, unpredictable, capricious and most demanding of all God's creatures.

You have the right to spend your money as you wish in an effort to hold back the passage of time, but, as far as I know, Joshua never did record his trick for the pleasure of posterity, so don't expect startling results. Follow a doctor's plan. Doubt what you see, disregard what you hear and don't believe one-tenth of what you read in those medical articles in popular magazines.

The race survived and prospered for generations before hormones and vitamins were discovered, though, of course, people used to eat more simple foods and it wasn't so far from the cow to the table.

20

The lengthening shadow of the boy

As we grow old we become more foolish and more wise.

La Rochefoucauld

In one of his stories O. Henry wrote that life was a series of circles, and that printed on the back of the sign that read "start" was the word "finish." You got off to a good start, so by this time you should be giving more thought to the years ahead.

Once again you must define your goal and decide the best way to reach it, for there is still time to make certain changes. There is no better way than to get out that old herd book and use the inventory you made in it as a road map to plot your route.

That old record of a youth's dreams may sound pretty silly to such a sophisticated individual as you believe yourself to be, but consider them carefully anyhow, and you may be pleasantly surprised.

The boy revealed in that inventory was the real you, no

matter how far you have gone or how much you have deviated from your planned route. That same man lives beneath the veneer you have acquired over the years, and the coating of sophistication wears off pretty fast on the rocks of the descending path.

The boy is father to the man. Napoleon's teachers may have been surprised when he became Emperor, but one of them noted on his school report card that he was "domineering and imperious." It's also a matter of record that Nappy was the leader of his neighborhood gang, and was often ruthless in victory.

As a man travels toward his second childhood it becomes all the more apparent that the boy is father to the man. I used to wonder how men reared in truly devout families could have drifted so far afield in adult years, and how, once they began to ease up in the chase after the dollar, they so quickly could slip back into the beliefs and standards of deportment of their upbringing.

Study your inventory carefully, remembering that an old man's pleasures, like his memory, tend to revert to the days of his youth, although some of the boy's ambitions, no longer practical, must be set aside.

If you have kept your inventory up to date, you will find that you have made many changes in evaluating yourself and your wife as time has passed. Now rewrite the personality angle all over again and strike a trial balance. This is the last time you will need this information, so give it plenty of time and thought.

After you have done so, record your answers to the following questions:

1. Are you most happy in crowds or at parties?
2. Do you like to prance around with other aged juveniles, playing softball or pitching horseshoes?

3. Do you enjoy meeting strangers and can you make quick friendships?

4. Have you enough money to keep up with the crowd in a swanky old folks' settlement?

5. Do you think you would enjoy sitting on a bank catching fish all day three hundred days a year?

6. Do you think you missed your calling—that you should have been a tramp sleeping behind a different pile of railroad ties every night?

7. Are you willing to give up many of the symbols of prosperity that mean so much to everyone you know—swimming pools, mink coats for your wife, and flashy new automobiles?

8. Can you watch other folks sail by in new cars without an overpowering feeling of envy and resentment?

9. Do you enjoy the comradeship of a few friends without having that enjoyment depend on a golf game?

10. Can you sit under a tree and talk to a man for an hour without exhausting yourself thinking up something to discuss?

11. Are you interested in nature and do you enjoy watching her unfold her secrets in the land about you, whether on desert or tropical isle?

12. Can you retire at night, leaving your worries on the coffee table to be picked up in the morning along with your glasses and false teeth?

13. Would you like a little time to sit down and try to figure out just what this life is all about?

14. Can you sit on a park bench and enjoy the crowds going by just as much as you would seeing actors on TV trying to act like some of the people you see?

15. Are you happy in your own company, or do you bore yourself?

16. Do you and your wife love each other enough to fulfill that promise to "forsake all others"?

17. Do you think that you could be shipwrecked together for weeks without tiring of each other's company?

18. Have you any serious physical handicaps?

19. Do either of you or your near relatives show marked inability to adjust to new situations?

20. Do you love your work and hate the thought of ever being separated from it?

If there are many no's in the first four questions, you'd better not plan to join a big, senior citizen settlement when you retire. Keep away from St. Petersburg, Florida.

If you answered questions five through fourteen in the negative, it will point to the life you want to lead.

If questions fifteen to seventeen, inclusive, are answered in the affirmative, you are lucky and can get by any place for any length of time.

The last three promise happiness if answered negatively, provided they are combined with an affirmative answer for the two previous questions.

If there are too many no's, you'd better take stock again; it might be better for you not to bother preparing yourself for retirement at all.

At the sixty-fifth mile post the road turns sharply and leads down the dugway to the valley. When you catch a glimpse of it on the road ahead, you can shut your eyes, ram the gas throttle down hard on the floorboard and hit the spot going eighty miles an hour. If so, you will land with a bigger splash when you hit the rocks that jut from the cliff's face below.

There's a lot to be said for such a grand flourish as you wind up your journey. It's a masculine way of meeting problems and would save the kids a lot of worry about having to take care of you in your extreme old age if you are not self-sufficient. It may also save you rheumatic pains, many lonesome days, and an ending that will probably be more drawn out and cursed with suffering from a wasting disease.

But I am a physician and, as such, must do what I can to prolong life. Whether pleasure and satisfaction or disappointment and agony await you is none of my business.

I can advise you how to prepare for this major step and warn you of some of the danger signals to watch out for, along with the whereabouts of rough places I have encountered. But I cannot go along and hold your hand, and neither can anybody else—not even a most paternalistic government.

It's a journey of interest only to you and your wife. Here, as never before you are the master of your fate, the captain of your soul.

Just be sure you don't let yourself get rimrocked on the way down.

21

Killing time is suicide

The statesman, lawyer, merchant, man of trade,
Pants for the refuge of some rural shade.
COWPER

Man's great trouble, when he thinks of retiring, is the boy within him. He regards the coming change just as he did a school summer vacation—all swimming, loafing and eating watermelons down by the old swimming hole. Insurance people have encouraged this dream by calling his retreat from active life "The Golden Years of Retirement."

All that glitters, when the sun of advertising shines on it, is not gold, especially when there is no parental table and shelter to go home to at night after the fish quit biting.

Your government would have you believe that social security was invented to replace the providers of your childhood, but if you take a good look at this legislation you will see that it was enacted at the demand of labor leaders who wanted older men weeded out of industry because they still had some self-determination in their make-up and did not accept the rulings from on high so readily as younger men.

If it was so good for the country, why was it made to affect everyone but the law-makers themselves? It's a wonder the Almighty didn't strike down the senile old hypocrites, some of whom should have been wheeled into the legislative chambers when they voted that all men should be retired at the age of sixty-five because they were no longer either mentally or physically agile enough to screw a nut on a bolt.

Things are stacked against retired folk; every time the price of steel goes up, social security goes down, even if they don't have to buy nails or iron fence posts. Since steel workers get an extra dime a day, so must milk truck drivers, and milk goes up a cent or two a quart. Thus grandpa has to drink his coffee black, because he is the meatball who cannot hope for a raise.

When I retired, I followed Roger Babson's advice and got a little place where I could raise a lot of my own food without having to keep up with the Joneses, but during the past few years they have been sniping at that little refuge, too. Fuel has tripled in price, taxes have followed close behind, and new laws make it illegal to nail a board in your house without hiring a union artisan to see that it is done right.

I sometimes wonder how sober law-givers are when they put certain statutes on the books. In Idaho, for example, there's a law that anyone wishing to buy a chicken after dark must have written permission from the sheriff. I try to obey the law, but when it prohibits shaving yourself, so to speak, because barbers need more money, I grow whiskers, even though I may wind up in the pokey for masquerading as a Greek priest.

There is one good thing about this high road to socialism. It will force more oldsters to keep active, even if they only raise their own carrots; they will live longer and some day may organize a union of their own, and, after gaining the ear of legislators, demand that rigged markets and planned economy be thrown out so that a dollar may once more become respectable. And as for the income taxes an honest man has to pay, all I can say is God help the rich. The poor, after all, can beg.

A raise in wages for the same work never helped anyone. When the Anaconda Company boosted wages it seemed that almost before the men got to the bank with their bigger paychecks, merchants had raised prices accordingly.

The gink who suffers is the man at the bottom of the pile who lives on a fixed income. His one break is that he is less hurt by a depression than is the heavy earner—especially the one who is deeply in debt.

It is my heretical conviction that depressions are a boon, and that continued prosperity will wreck a nation quicker than an aggressor like Russia.

I practiced my profession through two periods of great prosperity and two depressions, and the only time I was sure that man had been created in the image of his Maker was when he had to scratch for a living.

Most of my professional life was moderately boring, but when my patients were poor and needed my services I loved it, and the fact that I retired when my town was in its lushest period of war prosperity made that breakaway much easier.

My community reached its peak of achievement in good living in the early depression days in the thirties. The smelter was closed; nobody had much money; all joined to help the unfortunate. The town was organized overnight, and men with any income threw in ten percent of it gladly. The company rented a farm and the unemployed raised vegetables, while the farmers donated beef and lamb and everyone tried to repay every kindness threefold.

We doctors didn't try to collect bills, and cared for anyone who needed our services, while patients paid what they could.

One time that winter our back porch looked like the wing of a supermarket. There were two quartered cows, four lambs and a cellar full of fruit and vegetables. Despite all the food we gave away, it piled up faster than it could be hauled out. Laws were overlooked and young men went into the mountains and killed deer until we had so much venison even dogs sniffed at it.

Ulcers healed and there were none of those office consultations about sex matters. People were healthier in body and mind than I had ever seen them. Everybody was smiling and anxious to find someone less fortunate to help.

Nursing was no problem then. All the women in town wanted to get in on the act. I had only to mention that a family needed coal or clothing, and it showered down on them. Mormons were used to helping one another, but the Gentiles discovered what a satisfaction it was and joined in the good works with joy.

One old bachelor used up a good part of his savings buying groceries and clothing during the day, then sneaked out after dark to some needy home to pile the stuff on the porch. He would knock on the door and run. Nobody knew of his nightly visits and I wouldn't have found out myself except that he had to get information somewhere about those in distress.

Then came the WPA and all those government handouts. Everyone joined hands and raided the till. Doctors and dentists were allowed monthly amounts to care for the sick, and when we didn't have enough to fill our quota we would grab some kid and take out his tonsils or clean his teeth.

I retired twelve years ago, planning to live the next ten years on my annuity payments of a hundred and fifty dollars a month. I did it. My investments went up with the inflationary spiral and my income doubled. I still live nicely on it, but a few more price jumps and I'll be drawing on my savings.

What the poor devils living on social security alone will do, I zink maybe I don't know.

It helps, of course, if you have annuities and have converted all your life policies to paid up insurance so that there are no more bills to meet from that quarter. It also helps if you have some savings. A few thousand dollars in savings banks give an extra feeling of security, and I have made it pay, though my method might be considered risky for a man not up on medical matters.

Before I retired, my wife and I took physical examinations and learned we were in pretty good shape. I had received personal warnings from my heart, which meant that I would either live a long time or die quickly. Our prospective hospital expenses didn't seem heavy—for a while, at least.

We put five thousand dollars in a bank and left it there to cover the possibility of a bad guess. We took out no hospital insurance, and the gamble paid off. We got a hundred dollars a year in interest and saved two hundred in insurance premiums. Like any other investment, it was risky.

If you will have to depend on social security, save every cent so you can own your own home and not have to pay anything on it but upkeep and taxes. Every house needs painting, plumbing and carpentry at one time or another, and the cost of labor keeps rising. Learn to do some of the repairing, and do the job while the building inspector isn't looking. It helps further if you are handy around a car.

When I drove a Model-T, I could make most of the needed repairs. Once I burned out a connecting rod on the side of Ibapah Mountain, a hundred miles from Wendover, Utah, the nearest town. I cut a patch out of my leather leggings, soaked it in oil, used it for a metal lining for the bearings and drove home. Try doing that with a modern car, though. I can hardly find the dip stick to check the oil supply.

Coax your wife to put up fruit and preserves and to do some

of the other things her mother considered routine duties. You will never know how far the kitchen has traveled on the road to dependence on others until you try to get back to the way people used to live. The good old days aren't as rosy as they're often pictured, but there were certain advantages. "We can put our children on wheels to see the world," said Henry Seidel Canby, "but we cannot give them the kind of home that any town provided in the nineties, not at any price."

Your wife can combine the present with the past as easily as you can. When we moved to our farm, I was shopping for a churn when Ruth solved the problem with a Crisco can and the mix-master; she could turn out a pound of butter with practically no effort.

As you grow older you will find that your wants decrease and that you will junk some of the things you once considered luxuries. You won't envy those who have fancy gadgets, and, like Socrates at the fair, you'll be able to say, "There are so many things I don't need."

That tranquilizing pipe I mentioned will be cheaper than cigars or cigarettes, and will be more attuned to your reduced tempo of living.

That government check, plus the company pension, won't cover as much ground next year as it did last, but once you learn to live within your means you will be cushioned for the shock of any depression, because you won't have so far to fall.

You must plan to work at something in retirement, of course, for "killing time is not murder, but suicide."

At the age of fifty-five, you have ten years in which to plan. Spend your vacations checking the activities favored by your horoscope. If farming seems to be your Shangri-La, go to the country and ask a farmer to let you milk a few cows, and practice morning and night with the manure fork. In two weeks you'll learn whether you have a way with animals and get pleasure out of their company.

If you dream of a life of fishing, drop a hook for two weeks straight, with no time off because of bugs or bad weather, and eat the mud-cats, gars and turtles you catch. Then imagine how fifteen years of this will affect you.

Want to be a writer? Leave your family and rent a room in a strange neighborhood. Furnish it with a typewriter, dictionary, thesaurus and lots of blank paper. Write for several hours a day, and at the end of two weeks mail your best effort (with return postage) to a good magazine market.

The rejection slip will be gentle and comforting. You will have an assistant editor's autograph at the bottom of it and can talk knowingly to your friends about the writing racket and quote the editor's comments about what is or isn't salable.

If you want to paint—well, paint. But, like all the arts, this requires solitude; the muse is a jealous mistress who will stand for no distractions. You may produce nothing, but you will find out whether the urge is strong enough to support you when you get bored with life.

If you favor woodcraft, get a lathe and power saw. It's better to cut off your fingers while you are still covered by accident insurance than to do so when you are past seventy and can't get a policy.

No matter what you want, try it. The only thing I know of that an old man definitely cannot do is toot a horn in a band. His dentures drop down when he puffs out his cheeks.

Now that the problem is settled, let's think about location. There are good arguments for moving to a new place, and some against it. Familiar surroundings give you a feeling of security, and old faces and friends mean less adjustment. But new surroundings and acquaintances offer you a challenge to make good, and every man enjoys the speculative feeling a card player has every time he picks up a new hand.

You are used to your doctor, dentist, barber and grocer, and you will feel like a cow in a strange barn when you move to a new place. Well, they will be leaving you before long, either in a vertical or horizontal position, and you will have to hunt up new ones anyhow. Old friends die, too, so you are soon alone enough in your native habitat. "The milestones into headstones turn, 'neath every one a friend," wrote James Russell Lowell.

In a new settlement you can pick new friends as you would choose dishes in a cafeteria. Cultivate persons you like, and forget to return calls on the rest. If you select persons of your own financial bracket you will be content. In your former hamlet most of your friends were engaged in like pursuits and made about the same money as you did. When your income shrinks, they may be stepping too high for you, so you'd probably have to find other friends anyway. And if you move, it will save the agony of seeing some young sprout handling your old job in a way that stirs your bile.

I knew the head of an equipment firm who owned a big house in southern California. He sold it and moved up here in the brush because he couldn't stand the way his successor was running the business, even though it was booming.

Some persons don't want to move because it means leaving the kids in the neighborhood. Others move just to get away from the noisy brats. Don't shift your location merely because the neighbors' dogs bark at night and tear up your flowers during the day (and, when you complain, the owners are nasty). There are dogs and s.o.b.'s in every community.

Boredom is a killer, and if you move you won't be bored for a while, at least, because of the strange climate, customs and people. I have seen men retire from industry whose death certificates I signed a few months later. The old factory whistle had more to do with their passing than the disease I entered in the "Cause of death" space.

Most of them followed a similar pattern: a farewell party,

a fishing or hunting vacation followed by a week or so during which they told everyone how they were enjoying their freedom from toil. Then habit took over. They arose early and went down to see the shift train leave for the plant. Their old pals cordially slapped them on the back and told them how lucky they were, but they didn't swap much plant gossip, because there would have been too much to explain, and that always takes the fun out of a story.

After two or three weeks, about all the employees *emeriti* got in the way of greeting was a wave and grunt, so they gave up that morning walk. Now they were like the red bull in Arkansas that wandered onto the railroad track where an engine knocked him through the barbwire fence, severing his sex glands from his body. His owner filed a claim, stating that he used to be a red bull, but now he stood around pretty blue most of the time.

When an old codger gets blue, it's time for his wife to pick out her widow's weeds. A man and a sheep are the only animals that can lie down and die without rhyme or reason.

It took me several years to find the spot that suited my specifications, but I was anything but satisfied the first time I saw it.

I had listed things it must have. The first was an absence of snow. I had shoveled more than my share of that miserable stuff. Not that Utah had such big snow storms, being a desert country, but the stuff wouldn't stay put. You could drive out in the surrounding valleys and find the road clear and piles of the stuff out in the sagebrush, and when you returned a few hours later, the wind had moved it all onto the highway. A shovel was a must.

My second requirement was plenty of water. I was tired of raising a lush garden in the spring and watching it dry up and die in August.

I also insisted on a place where living was informal.

Beyond these simple qualifications, I was easy to please. However, I had lived west of the Rockies too long to consider moving back east. It's natural, anyway, for Americans to head west, and has been ever since the Pilgrims set out from England, so why should I reverse the trend?

Thus my search was narrowed down to Arizona and California. I liked Arizona's deserts and didn't mind the heat, but every time I hit Prescott I was greeted by a foot of snow on the ground, and I have seen Coolidge dam when a thirsty man could have emptied the reservoir.

Hoover dam was going to furnish so much water that southern California was to become a lake, so I bit on a real estate deal in Chula Vista, just south of San Diego. Visits to my property convinced me that outdoor living was impossible. Even on summer evenings, it was colder than a hound's nose, and the fog was so heavy it could almost wash out a bridge. I sold that property at a loss and tried Santa Rosa. Here, when the sun set, it was even colder. I wanted a spot where I could sit outdoors in the evening and watch the shadows fall without wrapping myself in a blanket. I also wanted a place free from those cursed chiggers.

And so, by a process of elimination, I finally discovered the foothills of north central California—a strip about a hundred miles long and twenty miles wide; elevation a thousand feet more or less; summer nights where you could comfortably sit outdoors until around eleven, yet with nights cool enough for sleeping; very little fog and about a tenth of an inch of snow per winter. Yet the mountains to the east have such a deep pack that water shortages are unknown.

To a guy raised in the rolling country of Missouri, however, and one who had lived in the level valleys of Utah, the ground looked uninviting. It was rocky and craggy, and the brush was thicker than in the Ozarks. But it was warm enough for orange trees and cool enough for apples, and the people there dressed as they pleased.

After returning during the summer and seeing the orchards clinging to the hillsides, bearing crops of luscious fruit beyond my wildest dreams, I exposed myself to a real estate agent.

Although I would have preferred a spot down in a valley close to a stream, I was told that such a location would be colder than the roof of an igloo. I gave up, bought a hill top, and have been happy ever since.

22

Check your motor and fuel supply

Look to your health; and if you have it, praise God, and value it next to a good conscience.
IZAAK WALTON

If you began thinking about descending the dugway of retirement at your fifty-fifth milestone, by the time you reach the sixtieth you should have a general idea of how you expect to travel down into the valley. Take it slow and easy, for the ladder of life is full of splinters, and they hurt most when you're sliding down. Anyone who has scaled a mountain knows that the descent is much harder than the ascent. Every step, whether you are afoot or on horseback, bumps your cervical vertebrae up against your skull until it feels as if they would break through, and a stumble is much more likely to be fatal.

You will reach the river in time, but most of us, like the Missouri farmer at a camp meeting, are in no hurry. During the services a laborer in the vineyard, with the true revival spirit, placed her hand on his shoulder, and in the voice of a cooing dove, said: "My dear man, don't you want to see Jesus?"

"Not tonight," the old man said. "Not tonight, sister."

If you want to get down safely, do what all experienced mountain drivers do before they tackle a strange, steep road. Test the brakes, check the tires, and then drive in low gear.

Take your aging body to a clinic and have a complete checkup before you start. Not a once-over-lightly, but the works. The examination should begin at the tip of your toes and work up.

As a man grows old, incidentally, his toenails begin to thicken, and if they tend to grow down into the flesh on the sides, there will be trouble unless you stuff cotton under the edges and train them to grow flat before they become hard and brittle. Corns and callouses should be treated by corrective footwear; many a diabetic old man has died because he clipped his corns with a razor blade and developed gangrene. If your job required a lot of standing on your feet, watch for enlarged veins and get supportive stockings before they cause ulcers.

If the veins in your scrotum feel like angle worms, wear a support all day every day. Watch out for a hernia, and if the wall of your groin shows weakness, have it repaired while you are still on the payroll so the hospital fund will pay for it. The same goes for hemorrhoids. Slice them off. While the physician is checking them, have him pay particular attention to the prostate gland. Sooner or later this damned little nuisance will make you wish you had been born a girl.

If you have a spare tire around your middle, eat less fat and sweets and exercise daily to melt it off. Don't worry about your old ulcer. It's good insurance, because a man who growls about his stomach all his life seldom gets a cancer there, and ulcers tend to fade along with the frustrations of employment.

Pray that your gallstones won't decide to travel, and treat your liver kindly by chopping a hole in your wife's frying pan. If your urine shows sugar, don't get into a tizzy, for exercise will burn up excess carbohydrates. Albumen and casts are something else again; consult your doctor about them.

A little blood coming from any place but your nose should be investigated at once, and you should have your chest X-rayed to check the outlines of your heart and to see if those cigarettes did any damage to your lung tissues. No doctor can be sure whether or not you will have a coronary. If it comes, it's a quick way of reaching the river, and speed is of the essence when you are ready to embark.

Your blood pressure is much more important than your wife's; if yours is more than one hundred and fifty over ninety, let your doc worry about it, but if your wife's is two hundred and fifty, don't prick up your ears and begin to look at the fillies in the pasture.

An interesting blood pressure becomes increasingly important to women in their sunset years. They keep graphs of its fluctuations the way an investment house does the price of stocks, and many of the old gals keep the record in their handbags. The one who can show the biggest fall or rise on the latest quotation steals the spotlight from her sisters.

When I was young and green in medical judgment I told one ancient dame that because of high blood pressure she might die at any time from a cerebral hemorrhage. Twenty-five years later, when she was a real antique, she did just that, but her daughters-in-law regarded me with fishy eyes during the interval between my diagnosis and her passing.

I'll bet I've wrapped that little gray bag around flabby arms ten thousand times, and nine thousand and nine hundred times it was unnecessary, but women—especially grandmothers—must have their little thrills.

"The large majority of people who consult you for treatment of heart disease," said Dr. Cabot in his book, "do not have it." That went for most of the patients who used to come into my office. Most of us are like the old hobo who leaned against the lamp post and said: "I'm an old man and full of trouble, most of which never happened."

If your teeth are bad, have them yanked. Artificial dentures aren't so bad as pictured, and once you retire, you can wear them in your pocket if you wish. Have your ears checked. I have seen plugs of wax in the canal as big as your little finger, and as hard as flint. Such a condition explains why some persons think they need a hearing aid.

An eye man should look over your eyes for opacities, cataracts and the condition of the blood vessels. Watch every skin blemish; brown spots will surely come, but if they are much rougher than the rest of your face, or there is a sore on the lip or inside the mouth that takes longer to heal than the usual "cold sore," see your physician pronto.

Your daily exercise will limber up those tired, stiff muscles and joints in your back and limbs. If you find your fingers getting stiff from arthritis, buy a cow instead of rheumatic remedies. Milking will help keep them limber. If you can't afford a cow, get a piece of sponge rubber about twice the size of a cow's teat and carry it around in your hand. Squeeze and relax your fingers when not using them for something else. Gene Tunney does this every chance he gets.

The older you get, the slower you must turn and get up and down to avoid nasty falls. It's simply a matter of circulatory adjustment. Remember, too, that your reflexes have slowed down; drive your car ten miles slower than your former average speed and you will dent your fenders about as often as usual.

I'm not going to hand down any commandments from my personal Mount Nebo about guzzling. The Mormons, who don't smoke either, are a healthy people, and they drink neither tea nor coffee nor alcoholic beverages. But there is no harm in any of these things if taken in moderation. For some persons, of course, one drink is too many, and a thousand are not enough.

I often prescribed a little wine in the morning for the aged, to help them get going. One old sinner tried to take advantage of this therapy. Complaining of aches and pains, he asked if I didn't think a little spirits might help him. I wrote out a prescription for a three-ounce bottle of whisky, with directions for two tablespoonfuls before breakfast. He howled, insisting that I raise his quota to at least a gallon. He went on to say that his wife wouldn't let him take any more than the doctor ordered, and he computed that four ounces of whisky added to one teaspoonful of water and sugar was the amount he needed to rev up his motor. That old fool got no whisky on my Rx.

This book is not changing into a handy reference guide for self-diagnosis of the ills of the aged. This chapter, like the Burma Shave signs on the highway, has just a few gentle hints to remind you that a sound body is just as important as an energetic mind if you are to get a full measure of enjoyment out of your retirement.

You can, of course, make yourself sick as a result of a physical examination, and you can cure some things by ignoring them. Corns, cancers, bum prostates and hemorrhoids are among the exceptions.

If you think the first doctor you consulted was too pessimistic, see another, but ask both to give you an honest appraisal. If they don't agree, try a third and accept the majority opinion.

This is the time for you to have your body put in the best possible physical condition. If you wait until you are too far down the shady side of the hill, it may be too late. If a hernia develops in a person over seventy, for example, I would advise him to buy a truss, for his muscles are probably too weak to guarantee a successful operation which may, besides, stir up his prostate. Correction of that may start his gallstones migrating, and by the time he is out of the shop, he will have undergone several operations. Each one would take so much from his allotted span.

If you are poor at this stage, you will put up with a lot of inconvenience and skip trouble. I have found that men who don't have to worry about living are inclined to worry less about dying, while the worriers rush to the doctor every time their little finger hurts. People do have diseases, of course, and there are preparations that will aid greatly in curing them, but I could count all the useful drugs on my fingers, and those that are effective by mouth, on the fingers of one hand. And I practice what I preach. In seventy-five years I have never swallowed any drug but aspirin, or any medicine but castor oil. Only out of curiosity have I ever taken a slug of any new preparation, and then only to see what the effect might be before I prescribed it. There are few preventable diseases of old age that cannot be cured by a brisk walk, a good book or a dish of prunes, and if you worry too much, you spend on doctors and medicine money that should be used for your wife's entertainment. Naturally, if you hound your doctor, he will humor you, but remember that when he gives you five kinds of medicine he may be trying to reassure you by giving you something to think about, just as you used to amuse your baby by putting syrup on his hands and giving him a feather to play with.

Think in terms of prevention when you are around sixty and you will be in good shape when you move into that rural shade. You will then be able to put your worry in mothballs and keep yourself pleasantly occupied. Remind yourself as you get ready for retirement that worry is a rut, and a rut has been aptly defined as a grave with both ends knocked out.

23

Whither thou goest, make her go

Three things that will drive a man from home are a door that creaks, a roof that leaks and a wife who scolds whene'er she speaks.

AN OLD ENGLISH SAYING

When I was a lad in Missouri, an Iowa family moved into our neighborhood. The father and sons melted into the picture as though they had been planted there; but the mother, a painful bore, kept comparing conditions to those in good old Ioway, and always, of course, to our disadvantage.

As a physician in Utah, I hated taking care of Easterners who had recently moved West, because my beloved country was sure to take a panning from homesick matrons who acted as if it was mostly my fault that this tumbleweed and sagebrush paradise didn't more closely resemble Alabama, Pennsylvania or Oklahoma.

Western gals were different! My wife Ruth and I spent our honeymoon in a mining camp, where rabid coyotes sometimes chased her around the shack, and where drunks from the nearby grog shop occasionally shot holes in our chimney in the middle of the night.

Our living quarters faced the rear of a greasy spoon restaurant, our sanitary facilities were on Main Street, my bride had to wash over a sagebrush fire on a hillside and we drank water drawn from the tank of a railroad locomotive. Yet Ruth, a true daughter of pioneers, with her gaze always on the mountains in the future, never complained.

She did gripe a little, however, after we retired to our California home early in winter. When February brought promise of spring, with almond trees flowering in the green valleys and pussywillows and redbud in bloom, she would stand gazing out the window at this beautiful landscape and complain: "Looking at all that green stuff makes me bilious."

Several things were wrong with the location; it lacked shad scale, skunk cabbage and fast flying tumbleweeds. The mountains were so blanketed with trees that you couldn't see the mountains themselves, and there wasn't enough sand whirling around to allow for normal breathing. It simply wasn't Utah.

When I took time to think about it, I realized that all creatures tend to get homesick for familiar surroundings, with the possible exception of man's vassal, the dog, who seems happy as long as he is with his master.

Men miss familiar places and old associations, but unless there is a lot of Mom in their make-up, they can quickly adapt themselves to new diggings, whereas a cow or a mare is not safe to trust with flimsy fencing around a new pasture until she has brought forth an offspring in the unfamiliar surroundings. By the same token, home to a woman is where her babies were born.

During the early years of her marriage, a wife will gladly follow her mate into the mountains of Tibet or to a Mexican mining camp, but a grandmother of sixty doesn't yen to see the other side of a local mountain unless she has a return ticket in her handbag.

Thus, if you have finally decided to move when you retire, condition her for the event, and have some of your battles before relocation. She may never completely reconcile herself to the change (especially if she is an Easterner), but at least you can say that you talked it over beforehand, and she never did positively say she wouldn't move.

Consider her feelings, and perhaps instead of thinking you married a dope, you will understand her attitude better. Not that this loving understanding should in any way influence your carrying out your plans. As noted, it is the nature of the distaff side to bitch about something or other, and you are kindness itself in giving her a theme that will never grow old or outdated so long as you both may live.

She made her exit from the active stage the day her youngest child left for college, while your responsibility continued financially for years. The arrow had been sent forth on its flight toward destiny, and there wasn't anything more that she could do about it.

Her procreative machinery ran out of gas some ten years ago, and she had quite a struggle adjusting to the new situation. You let the doctor worry about that, and were helpful only in reminding her, on occasion, that all women come to that pass if they live long enough.

Now the shoe is on the other foot. You are going to retire, and you expect it to be as big a production as the launching of the *Queen Mary*. You intend to avenge yourself for all the boring swan songs you have had to listen to by broadcasting at every opportunity your plans for your own business menopause.

And you can't understand why she isn't more excited about this proposed expedition into the Wonderful Land of Oz. Her lack of enthusiasm about preparations puzzles you.

Look, Pop, she concluded long ago that you were just a motheaten edition of a little boy, and she knows that boys are not very stable in their plans and dreams. One day they want to be a wild and woolly cowpoke when they grow up, the next day a prizefighter. Then comes an ambition to be President, write a great novel, and play a tuba.

She eyes the accumulation of tools for the proposed career with the same detachment she showed when the boys used to pack their bags and prepare to leave home when they were six.

This retirement dream, she figures, will also pass. Next week the poor sap will raise his sights on some new venture, and later there will be other visionary projects. Anyway, it will be about five years before his final decision, so she lets him dream.

During those five years she hopes that something will prevent your retiring, and she keeps hoping until she sees the inevitable gold watch. Then comes the let-down. The thought of having you around the house all day every day is just too awful to contemplate. She recalls the time you sprained your back playing softball and had to stay home a week. That was bad enough. Of course, she always loved to hear your footstep on the porch when you returned from work, and she managed to endure weekends, because that is part of a wife's duty, but may the Saints preserve her from week after week of Sundays.

Moreover, she has made some plans herself, just in case her prayers that you won't retire aren't answered. She doesn't mention them until she gets you in a spot where you haven't time to think up any good counter-arguments.

She has always wanted to see the changing of the guard at Buckingham Palace and enjoy the beauty of Hawaii, and has been secretly gathering information about such trips, even though she knows you get a headache when riding in any conveyance, unless you drive.

You might consider a trip to the islands if she would let you sail your own boat, or even go there in an old dirty freighter while you read Conrad and imagine yourself before the mast. But no, she wants to go first class, which means you will have to dress for dinner and spend endless hours watching a bunch of enthusiastic morons learning to do the hula.

You know before you start that she will prevent your fully enjoying the scenery. She'll probably remind you to watch the hula dancers' hands, because they tell such a beautiful story in sign language, not realizing that you didn't make the trip to look at hands and that, like most men, you would prefer that the dancers keep their hands over their heads all the time so that the view will not be obstructed.

She doesn't really want to go to Paris, but Mrs. Jones went there and bought such a lovely bag from a sharpie who swore it had been smuggled in from Rome. Mrs. Jones got it by customs by wearing it as a bustle, and that made her high woman on the totem pole until some other pious old biddy sneaked two of them in as bras. By the way, don't dare note that your wife needs no padding in either direction, or that she would be lucky to get by customs with an ounce bottle of perfume buried in the cleavage. And don't bring up the matter of ethics, or she will remind you that men never understand.

If you must take a trip, get some colored pictures of your wife turning green from seasickness, wobbling the lens a bit to make it appear that the ocean is heaving the boat around. Such evidence may be valuable next time she wants to travel, for an old lady is not at her prettiest when doing a waltz with an emesis basin. Your revenge will be complete when you casually show her this snapshot in the album of the trip.

Whether she drags you some place or not, she will be reluctant to give up her hard-earned position on the social lad-

She'll remind you to watch the hula dancer's hands because they tell such a beautiful story.

der. She knows that new hens in a flock take a lot of buffeting around before they find their roosting place. She went through all this years ago, and her beak isn't as shifty as it once was. She feels too old to start all over.

Shopping in strange stores might be thrilling, but she knows she would never be satisfied with a dress that didn't come from her favorite shop. If you suggest that the same line is carried in other cities, she will counter that the girls in this store know exactly what she wants. (Some stunt, because she has no idea herself as to just what she wants or whether she wants anything or not.)

She may also balk at your retiring because she has seen what sorry messes other men have become when they slacked off; she knows from experience that a listless man child is sick, and that a grandpa with nothing to do will pass out of the picture pronto.

And when she reminds you of all the aging widows you both know, you are suddenly shocked to realize that the "grieving" old biddies look surprisingly happy.

Well, you say, the guys who died so soon after they gave up their active careers didn't plan their retirement. Anyway, you have no choice. Since your income is to be halved, you can't hope to keep up with the old crowd.

At this point, she reminds you of all the things you can deny yourself. Golf is not only expensive, but also a waste of time. As Mark Twain said, it's "a good walk spoiled." You can get the same exercise by taking the mutt out for a walk, you lazy lug. Cut out tobacco and penny-ante; listen to the news on the radio and you won't have to buy newspapers.

Old wives, like engaged girls, are quick to notice the mote in their lovers' eyes and miss the beam in their own.

While telling you how to cut down, it never occurs to them that all those trips to the beauty parlor aren't paying off. When women wail, "I just can't do a thing with my hair," you should add, "And neither can the beauticians."

When the time comes for you to move, however, your wife won't balk. She has cared for you too long to desert you now, and she knows just what your boiling point is. She will yield before you start popping off, but, being expert in fighting a delaying action, she will campaign to the bitter end.

Chronicles we read about the winning of the West skip a lot of interesting narrative. They don't mention that the war-whoops of savage Indians were probably a welcome change from those that assailed the ears of the hardy pioneers whenever they got close enough to the wagons for their wives to open up on them. I'll bet those Eastern gals who went West in those jolting prairie schooners blew their tops, and when they reached their destination they probably tried to make it a facsimile of the place they left.

My wife's grandmother died while traveling to the gold fields from the territory of Utah, and I thought her granddaughter might avenge her loss by braining me as we passed over the same general route by automobile ninety years later.

For thirty years Ruth and I, like all doctors' families in a small community, had lived in a goldfish bowl. In retirement I was sure our lives would be our own, and that with good luck we could look forward to many years of a quiet, but most satisfying, second honeymoon.

But don't try it unless you are sure that your love for each other has grown rather than diminished over the years, and that you can spend many hours with only that familiar face to look at. "Before marriage," said Nietzsche, "this question should be put: 'Will you continue to be satisfied with this woman's conversation until old age.' Everything else in marriage is transitory."

Brother, let's hope you picked a good listener. That's even better than a good conversationalist.

If your loving mate balks, and you're sure of her devotion, grab her by the hair and drag her along. She is a Ruth at heart who wants to go "whither thou goest."

And let her complain as she goes. Let her look backward even as did the poor lady who had to leave her split level cottage on Sodom so many centuries ago.

She wouldn't be a woman if she ever stopped complaining for too long. As far as women are concerned, squawking is not a vice. It's merely a manner of speaking.

24

Bringing down father

Never look back; someone may be catching up.

SATCHEL PAIGE

Preparations for retirement aren't confined to such pleasant chores as riding over the country in search of a new home and browbeating your wife into accepting your point of view. You have to make some adjustments that will try your own soul, and since they are sad to contemplate, I have left them to this last chapter on the subject.

"To every thing there is a season," says Solomon; "a time to plant and a time to pluck up that which is planted."

Now is the time to pluck up what you have spent all your life planting. Now you must sever the cords that bound you to the life you knew, and there is no easy way to cut that binding, which must be done in your early sixties.

First, consider the children. For a long time you have thought that the kids should have been separated from the financial umbilical cord, but you got satisfaction from thinking you were still able to provide for them when they got into hot water and needed your help.

You and your wife are starting out on a second honeymoon, and children aren't considered an asset to such an enterprise in good society.

At this time, you must separate yourself from all parental obligations, with the possible exception of occasional baby-sitting for your grandkids.

Like the old robin, if the kids are still hanging around the nest, shove them out; but, unlike Papa Robin, don't let them follow you around the lawn coaxing for every worm you dig up.

Once your boy is out of college your business dealings with him should be on the same level and terms as those of his banker. If he needs money to start a venture, and you have it to spare, loan it and demand an interest-bearing note, or, if he has a car, take a mortgage on it.

This may sound harsh to your wife, but remind her that she weaned him once and now is the time for you to repeat the process, even though it may create a bigger fuss than the first time, since he can yell louder now than when he was an infant.

We all know of marriages that could have been saved if the partners hadn't cherished the idea that they could go home and latch onto the rear spigot again rather than adjust to the independent life which all newly married couples must have. Your wife considers her son a little boy to be taken into her arms and sung to sleep any time things don't suit him, and she tends to blame all his bumps on the ruffians down the block or on that nasty little cat he married.

The little cat rightly blames it all on her mother-in-law, and a good time is had by all, except you. If so, it sure louses up your plans.

The daughter problem is somewhat different. She flies out

of the home nest at her first opportunity like a bullet from a gun. Here, the trouble often is that once she has established her own home, she tends to boomerang back, bringing her husband with her.

Her mother would gladly send her packing, but she always was the apple of your eye, and unless you harden your heart you may cause another divorce, because no self-respecting young husband will stand for that turn of affairs.

A man I know settled this problem nicely before it ever arose. He had several loving daughters who clung to him long after they should have been out on their own. He told each that he would give her a home as a wedding present, provided it was located at least eight hundred miles from his. They scattered like leaves in a gale, and now he and his wife spend many happy days traveling about the country visiting their daughters' families; and when they get tired of that, they come home. His sons-in-law like the arrangement too.

Another man with sons and daughters who tended to roost close to home built himself a new house in a distant state. I called on him there and found that his dwelling consisted of three tiny rooms and a bath. "I built this house so small the kids can't find room to stay all night in it," he said. "Just weaning them, Doc, that's all."

You may think these cases unusual and insist on thinking that parents never get tired of their offspring and want them around all the time. Well, such parents are courting trouble. Wiser are those who try to efface themselves from the youngsters' view.

After I had written a couple of articles on retirement I had a lot of visitors and letters from all over the country. At least a third of the parents I talked to or heard from wanted to move because they thought it better to get away from the kids.

Nature intended that the mature offspring start out on his own journey and find his place without interference from others. As Longfellow phrased it, "Let not him that putteth his hand to the plow look backward, though it pass over the graves of the dead and the lives of the living." Fade from the picture as quickly as possible, and don't look back.

When our boys were unmarried, we loved having them come home to stay as long as possible. Now they limit their visits to three days at a time, and we are therefore most happy to see one another as often as possible.

Another thing, Pop. Don't make an ass of yourself, as I often have, trying to tell your kids how to raise their children or run their homes. Your daughters-in-law may not be so forgiving and self-restrained as mine are, and if they tell you to jump into a lake, you deserve it.

You had your day. For fifty years or more you were like the storied rooster that thought the sun rose just to hear him crow. Now, Dad, your voice is beginning to crack a bit, and there are a lot of cockerels fighting among themselves to see which one will have the honor of knocking you off your dunghill.

You can either descend from your perch with dignity and decorum, or put up a fight and wind up a bloody mess of feathers in the barnyard muck, for defeat is inevitable. "Bloody yet unbowed" is a phrase for younger men. After sixty, you'll look better unscarred.

You are now a capon in the barnyard of civic and business affairs, and it would be wise if you spent the rest of your life in good works. Collect money for the worthy projects younger roosters have endorsed, help pay for the preacher and keep your advice to yourself.

If you are a big wheel in a service club, the chamber of commerce or your union local, relinquish the job to a younger man and take a seat in a rear pew. If you head a business concern, the boys may politely kick you upstairs where you can do little harm. Go gracefully under your own steam; it saves bitter disappointment and frustration if you bow off the stage while the applause is still ringing in your ears.

For an old man who has spent years in the rough and tumble of daily living, slipping into reverse gear is a hard pill to swallow, but don't panic.

I think my own profession suffers more at this time than any other, because doctors somehow get the idea that they own their patients; and when one strays to another physician, they feel an impulse to rush out and herd him back into the home pasture. And patients will stray; the old doc was a whiz in his day, but maybe he hasn't kept up with modern tricks, so they drift to younger doctors.

I once had a good friend with whom I practiced medicine for eight years. His patients rightly worshipped him, because their health was his passion. Being younger, I was supposed to take on work he didn't want to bother with. If patients consulted him and he shifted them off on me, fine; but if they came to me first, it was a calamity, and he would pout for days. I was twenty years his junior, and since women prefer a young man to look at while having babies, I seemed to be stealing his practice right from under his nose.

When he moved to the city, he still expected me to send him every case that couldn't be handled in my little hospital, although I owed him nothing. I earned every dollar I got, paid cash for the office and property when he left, and my office help collected old bills for him without charge; yet he got sore every time he heard of a patient from our town going to another clinic in the city. I respected him as a father, but I was responsible to my people, and they expected me to send them to the best doctors possible. I had more trouble remaining neutral than Sweden did in World War II.

He thought and lived medicine, knowing and caring about almost nothing else on earth, and his twilight years must have been hell because of his grim determination to hang onto his practice long after his patients had decided that he was on the shelf.

It's another day, brother, and you are as dated as peg-topped trousers. Instead of squawking about the million dollars the younger generation is voting for a new school that will include in its curriculum the teaching of music appreciation, flower arranging and social adjustment, just remember when you were considered by the elders of your community to be one of the wasters driving the country to ruin by reckless spending for a new school building or sewer system. Vote as you please on the proposed bond issue, but avoid arguments and shun the speaker's spot at meetings where the subject is aired.

This new generation must find its own trails across the mesa, make its own mistakes and lose its way, and it's the same privilege you had. You had your day on the stage, and hollering from the wings will neither make you friends nor influence the actors.

Of course this generation is crazy—look who sired and raised it. It behooves us old goats to keep our traps shut, and maybe the kids won't think of blaming us for what we consider a sorry mess.

You have not been cast aside like an old tin can. If you have anything to offer in your afternoon years, you won't have to broadcast the fact. Your community may need your knowledge and judgment, but don't try to force these things on them. Let folks come to you and you will find that being of service will be a double pleasure.

My first contact with new neighbors after I retired was most gratifying because it gave me a chance to do something for them before they had come to my rescue in other matters.

A farmer who lived just below me had a cow that developed milk fever when a calf was born, and because the only veterinarian in the region was sick in bed, it looked as if she wouldn't pull through. The farmer knew that an intravenous administration of calcium was the only thing that would save her; he had the medicine, but had no idea how to use it. When his neighbor came up to my place and told me about the trouble, I gladly offered to do what I could. Both were surprised that an M.D. would compromise his dignity enough to treat a sick cow. Whistler, the great artist, infuriated a doctor when he summoned him to treat an ailing dog, and the doctor got back at him later by asking that he paint his house. Retired persons don't stand so much on ceremony, however.

Although I knew nothing about a cow's anatomy, they showed me where the veins were, and soon we had the intravenous set-up working. In thirty minutes, the moribund cow was up and walking. Everyone seemed happy that I had been able to do a favor for a neighbor without any thought of payment.

This was the beginning of many grand friendships which I still cherish. One neighbor knows all about the anatomy of my cranky tractor engine; another brings over his big tractor when I need it; and we all are happy that we live together and can be of service to one another.

I know a retired linesman who put on his climbing irons and went up a hundred-foot pine tree to install a neighbor's television antenna in a favorable spot. Another friend—this one past eighty—spends summers leading explorer scout troops over the rugged Sierra peaks to the east, and never once has he had an accident among his charges.

The older you grow, the more you appreciate friends, and the more you need them to keep the hours from seeming so long and useless.

I beat the gun and retired at sixty, determined to leave my patients before they left me. It was a struggle, but nobody knew about it except my wife. Like all men, I hated to be pitied, or to have someone say the old man didn't know enough to fall when he was shot. I decided to take it easy while I was still able to enjoy life to its fullest.

If you aren't already lazy, retirement is a good time to practice the art. It's good for your circulatory system and disposition, and you will find enough companions who are also traveling their remaining years in second gear.

This period in your life should be like writing an important letter. You write and rewrite, worrying and fussing about the impression it will make on the reader, but once it is sealed and in the mail box, your responsibility ends and the results are in the laps of the gods. You can go back to admiring the stenographer's legs. You can still do that, but keep it casual, brother, keep it casual.

You will soon find nothing so enjoyable as sitting at home evenings, collar open and shoes off, while you are watching television with your brain turning over in neutral. If the program gets boring, train yourself to doze when the hero is in trouble, and wake up only for the last sequence when the plucky hero gets the girl.

Cut the dog's tail off a little bit at a time. A man can stop smoking all at once, maybe, but he can't come to a quick stop in his business life without disturbing his physical and mental equilibrium.

Give yourself at least three years in which to retard speed. If you do, you'll be in full control of the situation when you finally reach the top of the dugway of retirement.

PART SIX

The Time for Adventure

It's not how old you are, but how you are old.
MARIE DRESSLER

25

It's never too late to begin

A little farm well tilled,
A little barn well filled,
A little wife well willed,
Give me, give me.
JAMES HOOK

Although a man of sixty-five years may be considered a business eunuch by the industrial policy-makers, he may be on the brink of adventure; and if he becomes a rocking chair cynic pickled in the brine of disillusion, he has nobody to blame but himself.

When I hear of retired men beefing because they have nothing to do, I think of Lincoln Ellsworth, who was a young man at sixty-five when he prepared for another exploration of the Antarctic. Your retirement years should be the fulfillment of your most cherished dreams, a time when you can do the things you always yearned to do once you had rid yourself of the shackles of daily living. If you find the routine humdrum when you retire, it's because you started out on a journey with no destination in mind, and because you don't realize that happiness is a rebound from interesting work.

As a little boy you found your universe in the sand castle you built on the beach with your tiny shovel, but somewhere along the line you lost your ability to enjoy the little things of life which, because they cost nothing, are too often ignored.

After the Japs surrendered, I turned my office keys over to my assistant, threw away my white office jackets and embarked on a strange journey with, I am sure, a greater thrill than Columbus had when he set out from Palos. When Columbus started out, he didn't know where he was going; when he got there, he didn't know where he was; and when he got back, he didn't know where he had been.

I, at least, knew where I was going.

I was going to a nice little farm in the California foothills. But don't you be rash and rush out to buy yourself a farm just because of what I am going to tell you about my personal Garden of Eden. You and I are different, and my paradise might be your hell.

At the age of eighteen I had longed to be a writer, but all the authors I knew were poor editors of country newspapers, and the prospect wasn't inviting. Besides, my family had suffered from my father's yen to paint, and I didn't want to wind up starving in a garret. Soon after I retired, however, my youthful ambition popped up again, and, more as a gag than anything else, I wrote an article for the *Saturday Evening Post*. If they had paid me seven dollars and fifty cents instead of the seven hundred and fifty I received, I think I would have been almost as elated, but don't tell the editors I said so. In the following two years I sold the *Post* five thousand dollars worth of articles, and had just about concluded that I was the Grandma Moses of the magazine field when I ran out of gas.

My articles concerned themselves with my little farm, which was very new and real to me at the time, and with my experiences as a physician among the Gosiute Indians, a most interesting and droll tribe who knew as little about white men and his medicine as I did about them.

My stories were thirty years apart in time of occurrence, but like most old codgers, I could remember things that happened in my extreme youth better than those which took place a year before. The interval between thirty and sixty was just a confused dream.

Soon after my article on retirement appeared, I received a letter from a man who said he had authorized the National City Bank of New York to honor my check up to $20,000, and would I buy him a farm? Of course I wrote him to buy his own damn farm, but I remember thinking at the time that his letter reminded me that most men dream of returning to the soil once they get enough money to live on it. Even President Eisenhower shows this tendency, and many of the movie big shots own little farms up here in northern California.

There is a story that describes us adopted Californians. They say the first year a man lives here, he is a booster; the second year, he is homesick for his back-East home; and by the third year, he is as big a liar as a native.

I have lived here for about twelve years, and any train ticket I buy will be a round-tripper. Maybe you wouldn't like it down on my farm, where in summer I rise before the sun, mostly because there is no other time of day when an old pipe tastes so sweet or when the birds sing so beautifully. Are these the reasons, or is it because at that time the whole world seems to be my own, and once again I have the capacity for wonderment, like the little boy who finds his universe in the face of a pansy or in the shimmer of light on the surface of a brook?

In winter I get up an hour before my wife, build a fire in the fireplace, and sit gazing into the flames while I dream. If I feel blue, I recall the many asinine tricks I have been guilty of, and cheer up by laughing at myself. If unreasonably cheerful, I think of all the things I should have done and didn't. It's like a stage play, with me sitting in the balcony watching myself play many parts, and lousing up most of them; but here I find solace and peace of mind, two priceless ingredients for a full life. From this vantage point, what once seemed such a serious melodrama now looks like a farce. I tell myself that mistakes cannot be rectified and that minor achievements have lost their importance, that my health is good and that I have plenty of food for my soul and body.

I go down into the ravine to enjoy the company of my favorite bird who loves the sound of my saw biting into green live oak. He is some kind of wood wren, about twice as large as a house wren but with the same coloring and perky tail. He shows up as soon as I begin operations and often perches on the log I am sawing, apparently as interested in my remarks as my grandchildren should be but aren't. He is a good companion who never interrupts me, except to flick his tail when I make a puzzling remark. And he keeps his troubles to himself. Quail and pheasants may walk by, but this wren sits and listens.

I like the new life. You would, too, if you enjoy your own company and get a kick out of communing with nature. Just be sure that your wife does also, or she may get cabin fever and brain you with an axe.

There are lots of ways to find contentment in the years of retirement. William H. Gannett, the publisher who retired at the age of seventy, made history in the magazine field, but it was not until he gave up the active reins of his business that he was able to follow closely the growth of aviation. He never recovered from the thrill of making a balloon ascent earlier in life, but he wasted so much time making money that he could not indulge his hobby until he retired. At the age of eighty-five, he was still making flights.

Retirement may find you running a ski lodge, raising and selling chinchillas, refinishing and merchandising the antiques you had so much fun picking up at auctions; or perhaps you have discovered that your hidden talent for painting oils is paying unexpected dividends. Israel Litwak made his living as a cabinetmaker, and did not begin to paint until he was sixty-eight. Ten years later he was still selling portraits for several hundred dollars. If you have planned for your years of retirement, you will find that old age is the time for adventure. You will not only have fun, but will also derive great satisfaction from doing a job that everyone said was impossible for an old man. I heard of a guy named William Parmele who, at the age of seventy-one, rode his bicycle from New York City to Chicago, just to prove he wasn't yet ready for the shelf. Your ambition, I trust, will be of a more practical nature, since you intend to take your wife along with you into your afternoon years, and maybe she wouldn't look too dignified riding tandem at her age.

Soon after my wife and I settled in our new California home, a psychiatrist friend from Salt Lake City visited us, and we had a grand time for several days. After he left, my wife said he had quizzed her thoroughly regarding my actions, periods of depression and fits of temper. He thought, I suppose, that my giving up a good practice at sixty and moving to a farm was evidence that I might need his professional services.

She told him that, if anything, the old volcano erupted less often than usual, and there was less fire and brimstone in the air than at any time during the preceding decade. The psychiatrist kept right on working, and for the past few years has been an invalid, while I haven't been sick four times since moving here, and then only with colds contracted from visitors.

Fifteen years ago, I knew most of the doctors in Salt Lake

City. Today, only two or three of my contemporaries remain. Most physicians regard retirement as medicine to be prescribed for others, but never to be taken by themselves. Only we crazy guys ever quit while we can still walk.

Like most members of my profession, I have never been too sure of my ultimate destination, or of which of the many church denominations had the true road map to that glorious vacation land, so to assure myself of a bit of paradise I decided to manufacture some of my own, and the close association with my wife and the thousands of nights of sleep without interruption from telephones, doorbells and honking horns, add up to a pretty good substitute for the real article, particularly as I never did care for harp music.

Now let's return to life's roadway for a moment . . .

You are now sixty-five and ready to start down that perilous dugway to retirement. You are aware of the hazards along the way, many of them not evident until you are close upon them. The road winds sharply around the edge of a rock formation that was too hard to blast out of the way, and the view ahead is limited as you make the turn. Another car may be coming up the hill directly in your path, or you may come upon a herd of sheep or a couple of fawns playing. A rock slide may be a hazard. Thus, besides having your car in good mechanical condition, you must have your wits about you to avoid a collision.

It's a documented fact that many highway accidents are caused by family arguments that distract the driver's attention. The danger is much greater when you are on such a perilous road as this unfamiliar dugway. If you and your wife bicker while traveling this road to retirement, you may come cropper.

At this time, examine your conjugal relationship a bit more closely, remembering that you are no longer the answer to a maiden's prayer. If you think you are indispensable, it may jar you to know that, once you are gone, a fat, wheezy little dog or a mangy old cat will replace you as beneficiary of her maternal instincts. Pets can take the place of husbands, you know. When Marie Corelli was asked why she never got hitched, she said: "There is no need, for I have three pets at home which together answer the same purpose as a husband. I have a dog which growls all morning, a parrot which swears all afternoon, and a cat which comes home late at night."

You are a burden to your wife now, and it is little more than habit that keeps you both going along together like a team of old work horses that are used to being side by side—*so* used to it that they keep that relative position even when turned out to graze in the pasture.

Once you are out there with your loving wife, habit will make the old mare raise her head and look around for you occasionally, but she won't miss a mouthful of grass from worry about your absence. I have mentioned that widows seem to get along nicely and enjoy the calm after the storm. The fact is, brother, that although your marriage may have been made in heaven, it was more likely the result of the accident of propinquity, a common liking for sour cream on baked potatoes, or the rosy picture of a lifetime together that was painted by your wife.

Sex started the bonfire, your children's dependence kept it burning, and your pay check furnished the draft that kept the embers glowing long after the flame died out.

An aged widower is as helpless as a baby, as trusting as a stray puppy. He will chase any female who pats him on the head, and if not quickly taken in tow by some widow, will get so careless of his person that even a billy goat will shun his company. His children, of course, still love him, but they have problems of their own, and taking him in would multiply them. An old man, like a bobcat, never does well in captivity.

So just remember, when you head for that dugway, that although your wife used to cling to your strong arm for protection and care, the positions are now reversed. She is your comforting rod and staff, and she alone spares you the oblivion of a rest home.

Now, then, is the time for you to think back to your wedding vows when you promised to cherish her. Revive all the tricks of courtship which have lain dormant for forty years. Praise her cooking, admire her hair-do, buy her surprise presents and be as gentle with her as you were before marriage.

Don't do all these things at once, however, or she will suspect your sincerity and think you have been up to some mischief with the widow down the block (unless that seems impossible to her). And the shock of your resurrected devotion may kill her. Make a new concession every week, but occasionally rebel, because even an aged woman enjoys a fight before victory. Naturally, you can no longer follow your old custom of starting a fight at breakfast, then slamming the door and rushing off to the office before she has time to warm up her heavy artillery. Now you must fight it out on her chosen battlefield.

It's hard for you to accept the fact, but your wife is now the only person on earth who cares half a damn whether you get up or not in the morning; she is the sole listener whose duty requires her to sit through your long-winded dissertations on what is wrong with the country. It was Turgenev who said, "I would give up all my fame and all my art if there were one woman who cared whether or not I came home late for dinner."

Compare your fortunate situation with an old gentleman patient I had. A big party was planned for his golden wedding anniversary, and though I didn't care much for his wife, I wanted to be present to honor him. The stork changed my

An aged widower is as helpless as a baby.

plans, however, and the next time he came into my office I offered tardy congratulations.

"That party didn't mean a damn thing to me," he said. "I hated that woman for forty-nine years, eleven months and twenty-nine days, and one more day made no difference."

To be shipwrecked on the island of matrimony under such circumstances must have been undiluted hell.

A happy conjugal relationship, then, is one key to your happy retirement years. The second key is associated with pride. You must have a feeling of belonging and you must feel useful. In a hymn book my grandfather gave my father when he was a lad is this verse:

Whatso'er afflictions seize us
They shall profit, if not please;
But Oh! defend, defend us, Jesus,
From security and ease.

Don't expect your social security checks to add up to happiness. You must discover your own methods of keeping pleasantly entertained, and I hope you're more original than a lot of old duffers I know who claim that they accomplish this by going around visiting the sick and infirm. The human animal can stand a lot of punishment even when sick, so their good works seldom inflict permanent injury. If this activity satisfies their buried missionary spirit, then it's all right.

In retirement, I am not myself immune to good works, I hope. The master of our local lodge keeps a list of us old relics who are available when a stranger in the neighborhood dies and his family wishes our lodge to conduct final services. Since we are too old to attend lodge meetings, these occasions give us a chance to see each other with our shoes shined and wearing neckties. A good crowd turns up to show their respects for the departed, and it is a good opportunity for us oldsters to study the decorating job done on the remains and to wonder how the same finish would look on our own craggy features.

In this connection, I have warned my wife that there must be no tinting of my few platinum-blond locks of hair, and if maiden pink is a union requirement among morticians, I want mine put on my nose instead of my cheeks. Somebody should be allowed to enjoy the proceedings.

I once knew of a break-up, in what promised to be a happy union, because the funerals this couple attended lacked audience appeal. A poor old bloke back home advertised for a wife and got one, but she left him after three months, complaining that life with him was too dull.

"She just walked out on me," he told his doctor, "because I would do nothing to entertain her; but while she was here I took her to every funeral in town."

26

Go native and save money

To make a man happy, add not to his possessions, but subtract from the sum of his desires.

SENECA

When we bought our homestead in nineteen forty-five, there were twenty acres of oak brush and a nice little house. I fenced off seven more acres and sold the rest for a hundred dollars an acre. Five years later, the land was worth three times that much for building lots. Folks get rich buying things from me, for it seems that everything I ever sold went up the next day.

I wound up with a farm consisting of a hilltop, some nice oak trees, an acre of wild blackberry bushes and poison oak scattered around; a densely wooded little ravine running through the place acted as a bumper when the animals or I fell on the hillside pastures and rolled down.

The next three years were, I am sure, my happiest. My health got so bad I figured I needed four vacations a year instead of one, and I spent all of them fooling around on my new property. I took colored slides of every tree and bush on the place, drew maps and even tried to work in the contour lines with an old map board I had used during my army training.

Then I threw a party for my old farmer friends, who looked with horror at the steep hillsides which I expected to farm. They came up with only one piece of advice which I heeded: they insisted that I place my barn on the highest hill, regardless of the inconvenience, contending that a thirty-degree slope would eliminate the nuisance of mud. It didn't, but it helped some.

My idea of a barn was an old, two-story Missouri-type structure, with the hay mow on the second floor so that the dust and seeds could filter down on me every time I entered. This kind of building was a big help in other ways. I pulled my liver out of place putting hay bales up in the loft, and had the pleasure of climbing the stairs twice a day so that I could throw down hay for the cow. Thanks to my unusual talents as a carpenter, the stairs fell down with me a couple of times, but I am sure the climbing was good for my heart.

I left orders for the thing to be painted, and when I returned a few months later it looked like a snow-covered peak on a range of foothills. Right here I learned a lesson in color harmony which is so common in nature we seldom notice it. My neighbors' barns were all left unpainted, and weathered wood blended into the scenery like a hen pheasant in a briar patch, while this monstrosity stood out like a boil on a pretty girl's nose.

But man in his wisdom can find use for everything, and the barn finally found its place. In the deserts of western Utah, there's a big, lonesome mountain known as Pilot Peak. It had been the signpost for all the generations who crossed this wasteland from Jedediah Smith, the white trapper and explorer who named it, down to a certain green doctor who used to get confused with the cat's cradle of desert trails. I named the barn after this enormous pile of rocks, and when the country became civilized enough to need taxicabs, the drivers used it for the same purpose as Pilot Peak. When called out into the country, they asked how many miles and which way from the big white barn.

I had made a special trip down to the farm when it was time to erect this monument, and had some hot words with the builder about its construction. I wanted a well-braced roof until he finally got it through my head that the heaviest thing it would ever have to support was my own weight when I crawled around looking for leaks. No need to prepare for a two-foot snow blanket resting on it for weeks. It finally dawned on me that my snow shovel and tire chains were to join my stethoscope among my souvenirs.

The cottage-type house was plenty large enough for an old lady to care for, but it was dwarfed by surrounding oaks which were five times as high. One of our friends told the neighbors back in Utah that she was sorry for Ruth Peck's having to move into a lousy little doll house.

It was five hundred feet from the highway and a hundred and fifty feet nearer heaven. The road contained a few hundred sharp rocks per square foot, so that my first major improvement was a blacktop pavement that cost five hundred dollars—the most expensive as well as the most satisfying improvement I made.

I installed six hundred feet of water line around the place with many taps, most of them unnecessary. I built a garage and chicken house, and took lessons from farmer friends in butchering sheep and milking cows.

I dreamed of the day when I could provide most of my own food and accept the Lord's curse on Adam: "And in the sweat of thy face shalt thou eat bread." I also wanted to dress as I liked.

This seemed important, because for years I had been ribbed by my fellow townspeople if I appeared on Main Street garbed in work pants.

"Look at the doc," someone would say, "he must be going to do a little work for a change."

The priest could come into the post office dressed in undershirt and overalls without causing comment, but I couldn't even mow the lawn in front of my office without a bunch of wiseacres gathering to enjoy the spectacle.

Even after I had been a farmer for two years, a Mormon couple drove up to see us one day, and when the young matron saw me, she said, "Go into the house and put on some other clothes, you look awful." Those good old Saints wanted their doctor to look the part whether he was on the job or loafing.

I knew, of course, that in my work as a physician I used up just as much energy as most of them did, but the little boy in me longed for the day when I could get just as dirty as I pleased without being too conspicuous.

I no longer had to worry. Suits too old to wear to the office come in handy when you don't have to look dressed up, and there are no stenographers to look at you when you are retired. Old men are supposed to look a bit worn in all respects, anyway, and farmers can get away with baggy pants without causing undue comment. Tog yourself out in a fancy sport outfit and you'd look as silly as grandma does in a pink hat and toreador pants. At a Farm Bureau meeting, you would look queer to your neighbors if you were rigged out like a movie director, and if you extended your hand in greeting, a farmer might ignore it, remarking that he doesn't need any lightning rods today.

There are places, of course, where the master of the estate

struts around in riding pants and wears a dime-store Stetson. Such a synthetic cowpoke might call his hired man his "herdsman," even if there is nothing on the place to herd except a goat.

Farmers save money on clothes, then, as well as on food. Most of them need a new suit and dress shoes about once every eight years, and ditto for hat and gloves. The kids will keep you supplied with sport shirts and Christmas neckties. Work pants and shirts are cheap and easy to launder.

Also, you need a haircut only about once a month, instead of every ten days; and if you're as lazy as I, you will save on razor blades too.

Your wife's expenses won't decrease in the same ratio, since, having to battle that old "showing-your-age" devil, she will continue her trips to the beauty parlor and hairdresser. Don't suggest that she face facts and grow old gracefully. Once she feels that age is gaining on her, up go the food and candy bills and she spreads out all over the patch. You want to love and cherish her, remember, and those emotions are difficult to lavish on a dame built like a silo.

Don't expect to save much on amusements. You will enjoy a good show as much as ever, and the cost of professional journals will be absorbed by other magazines which you now find time to read.

Your automobile will balance increased costs with reduced activity. The year before you retired, you would have felt guilty if forced to take mother riding in a car older than your neighbors', but the day after you quit, nobody expects you to stay at the head of the parade. Now that your job doesn't depend on outward show, you can truly get your money's worth out of the old car; and though it may be news to you, cars don't drop their bolts and slump down as soon as a new model appears. I bought my car in nineteen-fifty, and upkeep for seven years has been limited to new tires and spark plugs;

the state lets me run it over the road for twelve dollars a year as against several times that amount for a new model. It travels along at a good fifty and gets twenty-five miles to the gallon. Of course, I do have to shift gears, but when you don't know any better, this isn't too much of a chore. Moreover, the car doesn't look as road-worn and beat-up as the guy who drives it.

When the price of fuel oil became unreasonable, I threw the decorations out of the fireplace and burned a little wood there for a change. For three dollars I got a saw and regained my proficiency in its use. Now every time they hike the price of oil, I saw down a few more oak trees, thereby keeping my fuel bills stationary while getting healthful exercise burning up extra calories.

Don't try to save by living in a trailer. Once we were exposed to a salesman who, after showing my wife all the household conveniences, asked her if she could suggest anything else to make it more home-like.

"Yes," she said. "Cut a half moon in the door." (This gag needs no explanation to oldsters, but for the benefit of the kids let me explain that such a decoration was once considered necessary for properly regulated sanitary outbuildings.)

Deep-freezes are all right for a farmer who kills his own beef and has a large family to support, but when you consider depreciation, spoilage and electrical current, I don't think they save very much if you have to buy meat. And I haven't found many honest folks who say they like meat that has been lying around for six or eight months. The same goes for fruit and vegetables.

Water and electricity? Prices of both are regulated by utility commissions, and since it is good politics to refuse rate increases, the cost of these items tends to remain within reason.

Now, if a little farm is in your dreams, here are facts to

consider when you try to cut expenses to your income level:

Older persons, like children, need easily digested food, so I figured a cow in my plans, and she returned me pleasure, food and profit. I kept Elsie for ten years, and she ranked with FDR's dog Fala in number of appearances in the *Saturday Evening Post*. I also kept an accurate set of books on Elsie, and her net return for the period was three thousand dollars.

I sold a hundred dollars worth of milk a year, plus a baby beef, and figured in what my milk and butter would have cost without Elsie. Against this, I listed her original cost, the feed she consumed that I had to buy, taxes on the pasture and water to irrigate it, plus a couple of veterinary visits. I did not take into account, however, the work required to take care of Elsie. That I listed under amusement.

Bonus dividends included cottage cheese, butter for cooking oil, and garden fertilizer. Probably safety of life and limb, too, since I had to get home before dark to milk her, and bright, oncoming lights, bifocals and slow reactions are poor equipment for night driving.

You can't follow my example in California, however, unless you want to be arrested as a milk-bootlegger. Just before I sold Elsie the big dairies pushed through a law that made it a misdemeanor to sell a quart of milk at a ranch.

But you can buy baby calves and raise at least two extra, in addition to each baby, on the excess milk, and thus realize the hundred dollars I got for the milk. You have to be fairly active to do this, because calves aren't so easily handled as you might think. A football tackle has the skills and agility necessary, I would say.

Another way to get around the law is to go into partnership with a neighbor on a cow. If you do, be sure she is divided down the middle, not stem- and stern-wise, since the front end is only an expense.

It would be nice to be able to brag to your neighbors that

your milk comes from a blue-blooded daughter of champions, but only Texas oil tycoons or retired chairmen of the board can afford such luxuries. Fancy cows, like fancy cars, demand expert treatment to keep them fancy. Just as you would buy an old but serviceable car for your son to learn to drive, so should you buy your first cow.

Any old cow of one of the standard milk breeds will give more milk than you can use, unless she has been ruined by an udder disease. Have a veterinary look her over before you buy one. And her disposition is more important than her pedigree.

Cow experts say the Jersey is the ideal for a family, and is more intelligent than other breeds; her nervous system is more highly developed, and if raised with understanding she is the kindest. But if kicked around, she becomes the meanest thing on four legs.

Our choice was a Jersey halfbreed raised by a woman. This cow had spent most of her life in a small pasture away from other stock, and was a doll. It took me a spell to gain her absolute trust, but thereafter she seemed to try her best to understand what I wanted and to obey my every demand.

Like all animals, she loved company, and when I was working in the vicinity of her pasture, she shambled over, begging me to cut down some high toyon bushes so that she could eat the leaves and berries.

If it was raining while I worked in my barn shop, she would stand with head and forequarters in the door, chewing her cud while watching me build things. When a strange car drove up to the house she would come to the gate to see who the guests were, and if I went into the barnyard in my good clothes she became excited. Even a new pair of shoes had to be examined and licked before she would go into the milk shed. It was flattering to feel that a cow would notice one's personal appearance.

Although my fences were jerry-built and poorly maintained,

she never tried to go through one in the ten years I had her. She liked to open carelessly fastened gates and made directly for the front lawn where she browsed on Ruth's flowers until discovered.

While acting as Cupid's go-between, the cow and I were often in disagreement. She thought only of the present, and I had to be sure the calf wasn't born on some cold winter night. She would voice her resentment by bawling all night as close to the house as possible, never thinking of stepping over the pasture fence and taking matters into her own hands. Her boy friend, who lived in the next field, had no initiative, either.

When I escort a cow to her lover, we divide the work. She drags me down the hill to his pasture, and I drag her back up to her own. Eight hundred pounds of unwilling beef on the hoof is quite a load to pull up a steep grade, especially when my wife refuses to tag along and crank the critter's tail.

Elsie's few ills were all my fault. I tried to follow book directions about feeding mash and gave her a stomach ache from excess feeding, and I infected one quarter by trying to improve on nature and enlarge the opening with a teat spreader. I had to inject antibiotics to clear up the infection.

The neighbors did not try to control heel flies, and she sometimes got warbles (a swelling under the hide caused by maggots). I learned how to prevent them from directions on the package of the medicine I used to remove them. Although I myself was subject to poison oak infection when I first came, Elsie ate so much of the stuff I gained a secondary immunity from drinking her milk.

She was twenty to my seventy when we parted company. I had farmed her for ten years, according to plan, and by then she was through with family cares and ready for a cow's ultimate fate. Needless to say, we didn't touch hamburger for a

She would stand in the door watching me build things.

year after she went to fulfill her destiny. You might say that only a simpleton would grieve over the loss of a dumb cow. All right, I was a simpleton. That dumb cow came a lot nearer to being a saint than a lot of folks I know.

You know about horse sense (including the kind that may explain why horses never bet on the human race), but you may snort if I mention cow sense. If so, you never knew my Elsie. From her I learned that as far as a cow is concerned, you must prove yourself. She returns your affection bit by bit over days and weeks, and once she feels that she knows you, goes whole cow. She will refuse to have any other person touch her teats.

Lead her into a new barn and she is nervous, and, realizing that this condition will hinder digestion, she refuses to eat. Cows, like cats, are often smarter than homo sap. When strange food is offered a cow, she will merely taste it to see what the effect will be before she loads one of her many stomachs with it.

If frightened, she messes all over the barn, yet can be taught to hold her urine when you are milking, all the while shifting from one foot to the other like a little boy in the same situation.

Absolutely punctual, she expects you to be likewise. Modest, she goes down into the briar patch to have her babies. Instinct teaches her how to care for them. She has a musical and tender voice when she communicates with them. She shields them from harm and when they are tiny will fight anything or anybody but you to protect them.

She avoids excessive exercise, asking only that she may live in peace and have enough to eat, while keeping two or three families in food besides the calf that has a rightful claim on her. She enjoys life and is seldom sick unless her boss is careless about milking her or leaves bits of wire around for her to swallow with her hay. When it rains or snows, she stays in the barn, and is old regularity itself in sleeping and exercising.

It grieved us to part with Elsie, and it was not always easy to part with the calves, all of which were cute and all a nuisance. It really made me feel like a heel when I had to make them leave their happy home, and bid a tearful, noisy farewell to their sorrowing mother. But boy calves are useless on a farm like mine, not to mention the fact that they are subject to stomach aches, which means constant care.

Milk goats cost little and require very little pasture, since they don't eat half as much as a cow. Two of them will easily supply you with enough milk, which, when cold, tastes just as good as cow juice, and is more easily digested. The kids make as tasty eating as lamb, if you can stand eating your pets. In this connection, I advise you against raising a single lamb. If you get one, get six more for company. One lamb is like one child. It is sure to be spoiled rotten and will act more like a baby than any other animal on the farm.

When ours was two months old, she began disputing the dog's right to walk at the side of his mistress, and at four months she hardly allowed him to tag along behind. She refused to be locked in her dog-tight pen at night until she had made a trip to the front lawn for a goodnight pat from her goddess, and respected nobody or nothing except the cow and us.

Forget the notion about a little chicken ranch paying your bills. Any time you try to play another man's game, expect to be taken for a ride. Chickens have broken more men than Reno and Las Vegas combined. They cost more than they come to. Besides, eggs shouldn't be used as a regular diet by an old man whose arteries are already clogged with the end products of cholesterol. I tried chickens, but Ruth wouldn't pick them, and when I picked them, I could smell the feathers while eating the dumplings three days later. Also, when five hens are laying there isn't room enough in the icebox for the eggs; when they are moulting, there are no eggs at all for weeks.

Chickens serve only one useful purpose as far as I am concerned. As they mature into old hens, they remind you of some of the fat old women you never liked. The more you watch a flock of chickens, the more you think of a Parent-Teachers Association meeting. If you want peace in the chicken yard, kill all the males and always speak before you open the coop door. If they know it is you coming, they greet you with gleeful clucks; otherwise, the air is full of chickens trying to get as far away as possible. My advice is don't raise chickens, but if you do, leave the litter on the hen-coop floor; they stay healthy, just as people who live in unsanitary surroundings seldom get polio.

Turkeys, although cheap to raise, are, except for guinea fowl, your biggest headache. If raised in a brooder they adopt you as their papa and won't even go out into the field to hunt grasshoppers unless you go along; and if you are cruel enough to leave the place for an hour to go shopping, they waddle over to the neighbors and eat up their flower beds.

Ours even insisted on roosting in a tree when grown. The tree was close to our bedroom window, and I suppose the old man's snores reassured them when owls hovered overhead.

When I lay down for a nap on one of my many homemade couches in the woods, they would wait until I was asleep and then perch all over me. A blanket of turkey feathers, plus the turkeys themselves, makes a mighty hot covering for an August day.

Kill and eat one and the others will stand at the dining room window peering in, all the while making mournful and reproachful noises. As for roast turkey, one twenty-pound gobbler lasts two persons an awful long time.

I like to kill and eat guineas, but catching them is a problem, and putting up with their eternal racket while they are getting big enough to eat, not to mention their miserable dispositions, is a trial. Hatch them out under a hen and they will follow her for the next two years and try to kill every other fowl on the place. I know of no more infuriating sight than to walk into the coop and find a poor old hen trying to lay an egg while five or six half-grown guineas are piled on top of her so that only her head is visible. There is only one way to stop this—wring a few necks.

For an old man battling high living costs, I don't think there is a place that offers more avenues by which he can escape the tragedy of going broke than a little farm where he can raise a good part of his own living. So far they have thought of no direct tax on the food a man raises for himself.

On a farm you can expand or contract operations as the need arises, and, if necessary, you can furnish nearly all your food. Persons of retirement age need three or four hundred less calories a day than they did when they were thirty-five. They are less active and, to avoid adding useless weight, need only about seventy-five percent of their former food intake.

Men, as they grow older, tend to revert to the weight they carried when younger, but wives have a different problem. Once past the menopause, excess food seems to accumulate about their waists and hips, while their appetites remain normal. If mother hopes to keep her girlish figure, she had better follow your example and count calories.

In my book, overeating is a greater sin than overdrinking, and a lot harder to overcome. When I practiced, I refused to take a confinement case if the mother gained more than twenty-five pounds in pregnancy, and I never had one case of eclampsia (convulsions) to deal with in over two thousand births.

Watch your weight, mates. Check it every morning and every night, but be sure those bathroom scales are right in front of the refrigerator.

27

Friends that don't gossip

When I play with my cat, how do I know that my cat isn't playing with me?

MONTAIGNE

Some of my friends nearing retirement age think a farm has one definite drawback. "Animals are too confining," they say. "We want to enjoy our retirement—to be foot-loose and fancy-free and able to take trips when we wish."

Well, take your trips and have all the fun you can, but just remember that wherever you go you will take yourself along, and if you don't like your company on a farm you may not enjoy it any more on the Isle of Capri. If you think travel is a substitute for happiness, check with your psychiatrist to see if you are one of the many geographical neurotics. Wherever you go, sooner or later you must come back to that lonesome old house where there is nobody waiting. If you teach yourself to enjoy your company, you won't have to waste so much time getting from one place to another. In whatsoever state you are, therewith will you be content.

Those who argue that animals tied them down are flying into the face of one of God's laws. He made man so insecure within himself that he cannot be happy anywhere unless he feels that some animate thing is dependent on him for care and comfort. Other human beings are the most satisfying and ego-boosting, but lacking them, any animal will do, for we love only those who depend on us. When there are no children or patients to fill this role, we turn to animals, whether cat, dog, parakeet or hamster.

I have known old ladies with plenty of money to travel who stood at the bedside of an ailing daughter-in-law and prayed to be forgiven because they were subconsciously hoping that, by some twist of fate, the care of the grandchildren might just happen to fall to them.

Every farmer knows that all his creatures have a personality all their own. Once you name an animal, especially, it becomes an individual, and although I am sure I could butcher a strange sheep or chop the head off other animals, making mutton of my frisky little Lilly Belle would have seemed like butchering and eating my own baby. That's why I say you should have several lambs or none at all, and don't name them or let yourself become overly attached to any one of them. I have never got over my reluctance to kill and eat my particular friends and companions. Even when the chickens retire from laying eggs, I leave the coop door open and let the wild foxes relieve me of my burden.

So don't dismiss animals too casually. Some day you may be happy to have some greet you when you return from a trip, and you may eventually discover that you prefer their company to anything a journey offers you.

Soon after we moved to my California farm, an old farmer friend, who had recently lost his wife, came to see me. We tried to get him to stay for a week, arguing that since all his children were married except for the one he left to run his place, he wasn't needed at home.

"You're right up to a certain point," he said, "but you don't know how glad the stock will be to hear my old familiar voice."

If, like a physician, your responsibilities toward your fellow man have been great and all-absorbing, the loss of them when you retire will be more of a shock than if you had been a lone wolf in active life. For this reason my medical friends all expected my experiment to fail, and some of them made bets on the length of time that would elapse before I began running around my new community with my little black bag. If the birds and other animals, plus the woods and meadows, had not been so new and interesting to me, they might have won their bets.

After we populated our farm with Elsie, chickens, lambs, turkeys, guinea hens, dogs and a barn cat, it was as confining as a monastery in Tibet, but we were too fond of them to be conscious of that fact. We accepted the loss of our freedom much as a young married couple do when the children begin to arrive.

And, like children, your animal friends will require attention. Your dog, if you choose to retire to a farm, will need considerable care because the barbs from wild grasses work into his feet and ears, causing great pain. He must be inspected daily, so you better equip yourself with one of those little flashlights (otoscopes) used by doctors to peer into a baby's ear canal. It will save veterinary bills.

Most folks dream of the country as a place where dogs can roam and frolic at will, but on a farm a dog's idea of frolicking consists primarily of killing the neighbors' chickens and chasing calves, and if they get home at all after such forays they usually carry some birdshot in their rears. Moreover, you have to pay double the value of anything they kill.

The best kind of dog to keep on a farm is a spayed female that has been vaccinated against everything; she will stay home and tend to the business of farming. A tiny male afraid to leave the front lawn is fine, but pretty worthless except to bark at strangers.

A cat is as necessary around a barn as a manure fork, and if she is kept there and not made too much of a pet, she will be worth her weight in gold. There is nothing, however, more worthless than a big lazy tomcat curled up on the living room rug.

My favorite cat has never touched a chicken or scared birds, but she craves gophers and rats. She will eat a bird that gets too careless, but will never waste time stalking one. She and Elsie were fast friends, but the calves were forever trying to suck her tail, and often wound up with scratched noses.

One cat mothered about a hundred kittens. We raised some of them, and Ruth spoiled most of them so much by playing with them that they were useless for anything except trying to catch the mother quail that nest in the shrubbery around the house. Our cat received the Puss and Boots award for cat of the year, and, like Elsie, had her picture in the *Saturday Evening Post,* although she was at the time probably the most moth-eaten looking beast in the county. She is all that is left of our many furry and feathered friends that did so much to help us adjust to a new way of life.

A farm is a small community in itself; you make new friends as the old ones go, but the older you get, the slower you are in finding replacements, and eventually most elderly couples find themselves alone with a cat.

I doubt, however, that this will ever happen to Ruth and me.

28 *Hints for fruititarians and others*

And add to these retired Leisure,
That in trim gardens takes his pleasure.
MILTON

Things that grow in dirt don't have so intense and binding a pull on man's heartstrings as the animals that eat them, yet there is a bond betwen the gardener and his crops, and gardens return a man's labor as much as anything.

A man can express his individuality by doing his own landscaping. I have lived in two houses built according to my plans and paid for by me, but the actual work was done by contractors. I did, however, put in lawns, shrubs and trees, and I kept kids from breaking them down and discouraged the neighbors' dogs from blighting the shrubs with their infernal calling cards. I nursed them tenderly until they were able to fend for themselves. Then, when the time came to sell those two places, I felt no qualms about selling the houses, but I did feel like a heel when I deserted those shrubs and trees.

Unlike beautifully landscaped estates and parks, and the geometric patterns of flower beds you see in cemeteries, they had a personality of their own. They were my babies.

Most regions, of course, have their indigenous grasses, trees, plants and flowers. Nature spent generations without number experimenting with all these things to find out what would grow best in a given area, and I am willing to accept her conclusions.

Any homestead you buy will be partially landscaped, too, but the previous owner and Nature didn't always see eye to eye, and some of the horticulture you find is hard to get rid of. On my present farm, the former owner cut down some oaks and planted nasty plane trees—bastard sycamores—and we can't remove them without exposing the house to the afternoon sun. I never will get through damning him for his industry.

After clearing the place of natural growth, I went down into a brush patch and transplanted a little manzanita bush on the border of the flower garden. Now it is the nicest formed and most beautifully foliaged shrub on the place. We planted many more expensive shrubs, naturally. No woman can pass a nursery any more than she can a hat shop, and for women graceful little plants have the same appeal that a windowful of puppies has for most of us.

If you have the natural reactions of an amateur gardener, you will over-buy and will soon have your place looking like a bear pasture when those cute little bushes become big shrubs and trees.

If your wife takes an interest in the outdoor garden, each spring will find you playing a form of musical chairs with the plantings. I never firm a plant in, usually leaving it in the original container for a year or two, because I know that next spring that shrub is sure to move.

We had one hydrangea bush which has completely circled

the dwelling in four years, making an average of two jumps a year and bearing about that many flowers per season. I also have several of the same type of shrubs planted in my part of the property, which bloom according to their own desires. They flower profusely, but, even though I bought both white and pink, they all come out blue after the first year and stay blue, no matter how much I fool with the soil.

We brought our liking for certain flowers from Utah, and, like most folks who move to a new neighborhood, tried to make a little spot of Utah out of our new place. Ruth insisted on myrtle, a creeping vine, around the border of her flower beds. She got it, but in two years it had us. I have been grubbing it out for nine years, and even now we are afraid to leave the windows open at night for fear it will crawl in and choke us in our sleep.

When you move, don't plant anything until you have had time to examine the native gardens; it may save you costly errors.

Winter-blooming flowers don't excite me much; they are pretty and the camellias are beautiful, but when I look at them I recall a letter written by an old Kansas doctor who retired to southern California in the winter. He wrote home that it was nothing but a flower-lined grave as far as he was concerned. They make me think of graveyards too.

Things a man should know about farming are legion, and once his brain begins to function like a farmer's, his ignorance seems ridiculous.

Being a doctor, I suppose I made more than my share of mistakes, but fortunately they were such that the only real harm done was to my ego, and in time I could laugh at myself.

Many years ago members of Congress out my way kept in touch with their constitutents by mailing them packets of seeds from the agricultural bureau. One old Missouri farmer received, among other things, some pumpkin seeds.

They grew and grew and bloomed and bloomed, but set nary a pumpkin. He wrote a sarcastic note to his Representative and in return received a note from the bureau informing him that he should have read the directions on the package which stated that these pumpkins should be planted close to another variety so that they could be fertilized.

"I have kept a bull who hated me for the sake of my cows," he wrote back. "I keep a gander who attacks me to please the geese, and, so I can keep the sows happy, a boar that will kill anything he can catch. But if the United States Government expects me to spend my few remaining years pimping for a damned pumpkin vine, it's crazy."

Pumpkin vines no longer need this sort of enterprise, but almost everything else on a farm does; so if you don't want to be counted as a procurer of romantic opportunities for procreation, don't read my chapter on farming. But remember that as a boy you decided to try everything once, and it is indeed a cruel man who would deny a poor little holly tree the opportunity to fulfill its destiny and bear beautiful berries, the symbol of our happiest season.

I thought I understood the birds and bees routine pretty well until I ran into a sterile holly tree. It blossomed faithfully every year, but there was never a ruby berry to gladden our hearts at Christmas time. When I explained my predicament to a neighbor, he advised me to plant a prickly little boy tree near the love-sick lady. We have had plenty of scarlet berries every year since we did that; that is, until the robbins migrate from the high country in December and harvest most of them before Christmas.

As a dividend, there are many little hollies springing up on our lawn, and every one of them takes after his papa.

If your wife likes to put up her own fruit and jellies, a few fruit trees and berry bushes round out the winter's supply of sweets. You must raise fruit if you live in a fruit area, unless you want to be considered queer by your neighbors. Otherwise you won't have anything in common to talk about.

But restrain yourself. It's easier to avoid nurseries than to pull out trees you have planted and cared for until they reach bearing age. There was a bare hillside sloping up from one side of my lawn, and, in an effort to break the monotony of the yellowed grass in summer, I planted a lot of peach and walnut trees on it. They do help the landscaping, but now I wish they were flowering varieties instead of fruit-bearing.

We waste many bushels of fine peaches every year because we can't even give them away, yet these trees keep me busy year-round. In early winter I have to prune and spray them and remove the grass from around their trunks to keep mice from nesting there and eating the bark. In the spring I spray again before the bloom, and all summer I am busy irrigating and thinning fruit. No man, by the way, should ever thin his own fruit, because he will be sure to leave too much and then have to prop the limbs up to save breakage. One peach tree of the early, mid-season and late varieties is enough if you don't like to see them go to waste. Graft all three on one trunk. These, along with apple trees, a quince, apricot, pear and a couple of cherry and nectarine trees, are enough orchard for anybody. (One of the cherries is for the birds, and the apricots will be thinned anyhow by a late frost.)

I mentioned robins. All the robins from the western United States seem to winter around my place, and a hungry robin will eat anything it can bite. They come ten days before Christmas and quickly harvest the toyon and holly berries, and then the fun begins.

With a cry of joy, a robin will swoop down on that camellia bush with its red berries as big as teacups all over it, and just as it starts to nibble, it discovers they are only flowers, with not a jot or tittle of robin nourishment in a bale. The robin looks just like a man who has been following a shapely pair of legs down the street only to discover that the face that goes with them looks like a gargoyle. My old cat and I sit on the porch by the hour enjoying the discomfiture of these naturally dignified and self-assured birds.

Every spring I offer up thanks that birds have the migrating instinct. If those robins stuck around, the job of raising fruit would be a shambles, because two robins can pick a cherry tree in two days. Think what ten thousand could accomplish!

In planting an orchard, remember that pears and quinces like their feet wet, while a cherry will die in a damp location. Also, wise up on the fungus or bacterial diseases common in your area. Notice the old trees on the place before you plant, and ask the county adviser about the dead trees, and what killed them.

In my region, fruit flows in like an avalanche from the first of May until Thanksgiving, and along in October, if I happen to bring an extra quince into the house and mention the word jelly, I am liable to have to eat the thing raw. My wife is a patient woman, but she refuses to adopt all the housewifely skills of her neighbors; she won't eat the raisins I dry for her, nor will she allow me to pickle olives, because she loves to watch the quail that live in the olive tree dining all winter on the ripe fruit. In return for this bed and board, the quail scamper across the front lawn like a flock of little old ladies crossing the street against a red light.

Unlike the quail, pheasants, along with turkeys, favor carnation buds and dig in the flower garden just for exercise. Hummingbirds love trumpet vines and jasmine. Everything that is raised seems useful, except oleanders. Even bees will avoid them.

Half a dozen rhubarb plants and an asparagus bed six feet square will save at least thirty dollars on your spring grocery bill when they are selling for twenty cents a pound. A fifteen-cent pack of tomato seed will supply your wants for five months out of the year.

For the beginner, strawberry patches make the most foolproof crop in the whole garden, but are the biggest nuisance to keep clean. Also, they have broken up more beautiful friendships between the grower and his feathered neighbors than anything else could do. They raise his blood pressure and make him use words for which he should have his mouth washed out with soap.

In the vegetable garden I have tried to raise about everything, and have three failures to report: Brussels sprouts, peanuts and tobacco. There are plenty of substitutes for Brussels sprouts, and I don't miss peanuts, for they attract gophers from miles around. After discovering that the tobacco I raised tasted like the bottom of a parrot cage and burned like lye, I tried smoking Yerba Santa leaves, and found them less offensive.

There is one hazard connected with raising your own fruit and vegetables: it spoils you as far as buying the same things in the market is concerned. I can spot the meat of a year-old walnut on a piece of candy, or an orange that has been kept in cold storage for three months. And peas, corn and even carrots lose a lot of their flavor if not eaten soon after picking.

But unless your wife is different from women I know, she will try to palm off on you those vile little green marbles they sell at the frozen food counter instead of going to the bother of shelling the peas you bring in from the garden. This is one time I advise you to do a woman's work. Shell your own peas, and go out into the country and buy your freshly picked oranges in season.

Raising a garden is easy and satisfying when you have irrigation water to supplement rainfall. One rainbird or other type of sprinkler will nicely water a circle eighty feet in diameter, and that much ground will raise a lot of garden. Weeds, too, if you prefer.

Because of the war, tools were in short supply when I retired, so I had a grand time browsing around secondhand stores in Salt Lake City, picking up those I thought I would need. Some were dillies: tin snips that wouldn't cut butter, pipe-threaders with all the threads worn off, and a bench saw which I have never been able to cure of cutting on the bias.

One tool every small farmer needs is a garden tractor, of which there are many kinds and sizes. I prefer a five-horsepower walking model, and use only the disc-harrow and mowing blade. Throw away the coulter.

When shopping for such an implement, don't believe all you see in those pictures of scantily clad maidens swinging their summer hats in one hand while handling the tractor with the other as they trip daintily over the land. A dame so clad coupled to one of those stubborn little burros would have her legs dyed black and blue and in splints before she went ten yards.

You can learn to handle them so that they will behave beautifully, or you can get careless and have your pants caught in the flywheel and land in the next county. Once you learn to side-step the jerking handles, you are on the way to becoming a professional boxer, for the footwork is about the same. It even takes skill and experience to balance a wheelbarrow, and patience to learn the art of swinging a hoe, so don't get discouraged.

When I got my tractor I practiced plowing a hillside. After the blade hit a rock, the handles swiped me across the legs and sent me spinning, while the machine, turning a complete somersault, landed back on its wheels and started to plow a furrow straight down the slope. Without even scratching the paint, it went right through a four-strand barbwire fence at the road, snapping all four wires and winding up in the ravine below against a big oak tree. Another of its gentler tricks was to tip over on its side with the drive wheel so fixed that the machine did the rotating and you had to get a rope to lasso the handles as they whizzed by. After I cranked it in gear, it knocked me down and ran over my leg, but its balloon tires prevented injury to myself or my self-esteem. Another time I was burned by the exhaust pipe while adjusting the belts. I also cut the head off a nesting quail while mowing in tall grass, but the tractor and I eventually got to understand each other so well I can now trip lightly behind it.

As long as I tend to business and don't waste time gazing at the scenery, we get along wonderfully; and though I cannot shave a peach with it, I can cultivate within two inches of a row of beans and never cut a bean with a disc blade.

Take care of your machine and it will last as long as you, and will give you much needed exercise before it decides to start in the morning.

Other tools will depend on how much work you plan to do, but be sure to buy one good hammer and garden trowel and four or five of the dime-store variety. The latter are for your wife and grandchildren to lose. As for your own tools, paint their handles red and yellow so you can find them when you forget where you left them. If the Lord had allowed man to interbreed dogs and garden tools so that they would follow you home, it would have been a much better world than the one in which science is trying to keep old folks alive and make bombs to kill everyone else.

An old man should confine his efforts and avoid accidents, and he should proceed cautiously. If I had taken the time to reach an understanding with my tractor before taking it out on a twenty-degree hillside, we would have got along better at first, but there were no books about old men and new tractors at that time.

The tendency to slight vertigo on quick movement, plus the slow healing of fractures in the aged, should all be considered before you embark on any job more dangerous than mowing the lawn with a hand-driven machine.

Farmers' wives have been known to go out into the field looking for their men folk only to find them pinned under a tractor, or with their arms caught in some other machine that held them trapped in its gears. The type of operation on the farm where one man works alone makes a farmer susceptible to serious accidents. Help is seldom immediately available on the old homestead, so the smart amateur is safety conscious all the time.

I read of a guy who, at the age of eighty-two, was treated for a fractured knee sustained while he was climbing a tree. During my first two years of farming I did things that were almost as silly. It took me all that time to realize that there was a better way to do things than by main strength and awkwardness. I went through the same mental brainstorms as did my remote ancestor who, tiring of his load, sat down beside the trail to rest. He probably kicked a log, and as it rolled down the slope he suddenly conceived the idea of sawing off chunks of trees and fastening them under his burden. This was one of the most important inventions ever made, for it made man more mobile, and therefore more apt to broaden the realm of his experience and get him into more trouble than was available before.

In my apprenticeship, I got sparks from the grinding wheel in my eye, fell off ladders and over rocks, and took many a tumble when I slipped on the grass. I mashed my thumb with a hammer and cut my fingers on a saw. And I had been in charge of safety devices in several plants, most of them engaged in such dangerous work as mining and smelting!

Today I spend ten minutes setting up my ladder on a firm foundation before trying to do five minutes' work while standing on it, and I no longer try to balance myself on one foot and stretch my arm just that two inches farther to get one more peach. In my neck of the woods, orchard ladders are called "vaulting poles" for obvious reasons.

When I chop a tree, I plan where it is to fall by notching the trunk, and tear down no fences in the process. I used to scare the cow, dog and turkeys out of the way before it was ready to fall, but found that one crack was enough to get them out of there in a hurry. Animals from instinct react to danger and seek the cause later, while we reasoning humans must know why we should run before we start, thus getting ourselves into all kinds of trouble.

When I became safety-minded I put railings on my hay mow steps, and built a ramp up which I could wheel grain sacks on a barrow and unload them by gravity, instead of lifting a hundred pounds at the risk of hernia. I also bought some grinding goggles after developing a healthy respect for moving machinery.

Last year I put a new roof on my barn, and since the eaves are eighteen feet from rocky ground I took extra precautions. Before climbing up from the uphill side to measure the length of the strips of mineralized paper I would need, I set the ladder up, went up to the hay mow and wired it to upright joists by passing the wires through cracks in the side of the barn. The next day I cut the strips into twenty-pound rolls and carried them up one at a time (roofing comes in ninety-pound sections). The following day I tied a rope to a middle post in the loft and passed it out over the ridgepole of the building, and when I got to that section I tied it around me like a harness, so that if I slipped I would remain suspended between heaven and earth until someone shot me down.

Then I put on an old pair of non-skid tennis shoes, padded my seat, and went to work. I never stood upright at any time, crawling about like a monkey or dog that has an itch it cannot scratch. The roof went on just as I wanted, and all I lost was the seat of my pants and some of the skin beneath it.

I saved about a hundred dollars on the job, had plenty of time to grow new skin, and had a wonderful excuse to lie under a tree for a week after the job was completed. It was a satisfaction to learn that it is never too late to acquire some skill, especially one that everyone said was impossible for an old man.

If you hire help, carry compensation insurance, because the damnedest accidents happen on a farm. If you walk up behind animals without speaking to them and startle them, you not only brand yourself a dude, but may also get hurt. A horse will kick and a cow with a baby calf will whirl around and present its horns to the intruder quicker than you can say "scat." A calf tied with a long rope is particularly dangerous. I have seen one so glad to see my wife she showed off by circling her at full speed. The danger is that the animal is sure to tangle her mistress's feet up in the rope and dump her hard, and since the tail bone in the female is more vulnerable than in a man, such an innocent little bump may half paralyze her. If you get caught laughing at her spill, you may wish she had landed on her face and had her tongue paralyzed instead of some other part of her anatomy.

An old fellow I hired to saw up logs for the fireplace got on the downhill side to work, and when he sawed off a chunk it rolled down the hill, knocked him down, and rolled over him. Had he been on rocky soil, he would have been seriously injured, but the soft dirt gave with his body, leaving him only frightened.

These are some of the reasons you should have a good liability policy that covers injury by animals and a compensation policy that costs only a few dollars a year and covers anyone who gets hurt while lending you a hand.

What has my experience on my farm taught me? It has convinced me that I can do anything today that I ever could, although it requires more time for the job and more planning before I begin.

Never have I been so happy. It took some forty years of marriage to fuse my wife and me into one individual, but this was worth waiting for. Love at our age is so much more satisfying and comfortable than it was when I was thirty. Now I am most unhappy if we are separated for a single day.

PART SEVEN

Twilight Years: Seventy-Five Plus

This is a woman's world. When a man is born people ask, "How is the mother?" When he marries they exclaim, "What a lovely bride!" And when he dies they inquire, "How much did he leave her?"

29

You're only old once

Old age, especially an honored old age, has so great authority that this is of more value than all the pleasures of youth.

CICERO

When you have reached your seventy-fifth milestone and are still going strong, you may feel a bit self-conscious about your age. You get the impression that folks who don't agree with you are apt to dismiss some of your conclusions as evidence of second childhood. This realization hurts like heck at first, but let's investigate this matter more closely.

Admit you are no Herbert Hoover or Bernard Baruch, and that you are beginning to see some things once again from the viewpoint of a child. There are lots of advantages and satisfactions connected therewith, and things to be proud of.

Once more you can be direct in your thinking and speaking. You need worry no longer about the impression you make on business associates. If a child dislikes anyone, he tells him so without any ifs, ands, or buts. Now you, too, can stand up and call any man a damn liar, unless he happens to be your senior, and even then what a pleasure it is to show him due respect, the poor old duffer!

A child is wide-eyed and interested in the workings of Nature, and though you ignored her until you retired from the madding mob, you should follow his example and appreciate her even more because you know the times are numbered when you can watch poppies and lupine unfold their beauty to the springtime sun.

No longer should a primrose by a river's edge be just a yellow flower that is liable to cause an attack of hay fever. It is the whole cycle of life itself, and a strong support for man's belief in the immortality of every living thing.

Just as a child loves to play in the dirt, so should his grandpa. There is nothing that gives more satisfaction than in joining up with nature and directing her forces toward yielding useful vegetables instead of worthless weeds. There is a pleasure not only in Byron's pathless woods, but also in having your hands in the soil, and this only the very young and the very old understand. It is almost as if the child recognizes that he came from this element and that his successful life depends on it, while the old man sees it as a soft comforter that will be tucked around him for his last long sleep.

It is the stuff from which dreams become realities, and whether they be dreams of mud pies and toy forts or green beans and cabbages makes little difference.

A child is interested in his bodily functions and is inclined to brag about a successful venture in the bathroom. Grandpa may not brag, but he walks out of there feeling twenty years younger, and he will swap methods of accomplishing the result by the hour if he can find a listener for his theories.

A little boy and his grandpa sit before the open grate, watch the flames, and see visions of the same thing: the boy sees himself as he hopes to be at twenty-one, while the old man remembers the time when he was that wonderful age. Both dreams are wide of the mark, perhaps, for the child may not accomplish all the things he plans, while gramps knows his memory has erased the unpleasant angles and has retained only the beauty of his young manhood. But they both have the right to dream. Women are supposed to remember pleasant things, men things that are unpleasant, but you can't prove that by me.

A child, proud of his simple accomplishments, calls attention to them if the visitor doesn't notice; his grandpa walks visitors down through the woods to enjoy the beauties of nature, and if they can't see the pile of wood he cut all by himself, he will direct attention to it in some way.

Everyone likes praise, and a little boy and an old man must especially have it, because they feel so insecure.

A child doesn't worry about keeping up with the neighbors, and an oldster who would have any peace of mind had better not waste time in this respect, either.

A child wants to go to bed and get up early. Gramps? Ask any daughter-in-law about the difficulty in keeping the old boy in bed when he is visiting the kids. Since he retired early, he has had plenty of rest.

Both are intent on worshiping their Creator by being on hand when He renews His promise of resurrection by bringing forth a new day. One flips over the pages of life's chronicle hurriedly and gladly, because of the wonderful promise of each new dawn; the other turns them over slowly with a sigh of satisfaction that he is still around to see it lit up by the first rays of the sun reflected from the face of the western mountains. The old man is glad he can still hear the birds sing and smell the aroma of coffee brewing—happy that three of his five senses are still functioning fairly well.

It would be a wonderful satisfaction if I could end this tale with soft music while an old man and his wife of half a century walk slowly into the shadows, the man half a step ahead, as is proper for the clan chieftain, his mate daintily clinging to his arm, performing her principal earthly function to the last—propping up the old goat, so that he may make his exit as he played his part: strong, virile, brave and magnificent, all reflections of a woman's praise and appreciation.

We need not worry about such a couple. Should one of them be taken late in life, the other is likely to follow before too long, because they have become so mutually dependent that neither can function without the other for long in the sunset years. I have known many such couples, and they are a grand Amen, the fulfillment of a dream.

Unfortunately, I am a physician, and I promised in the preface to picture man as I saw him. If I left him here, every physician who read this book would conclude that Peck was truly enjoying his second childhood, and that he was a liar to boot.

A lot of folks have not fused into one as a result of the marriage ceremony and the after years, and the surviving partners live on and on, eventually reaching the crowded and dismal rest homes, the foul-smelling senile wards of a county hospital, or, saddest of all, the wards of insane hospitals. Any old place where their kids don't have to take care of them.

In *The Horse and Buggy Doctor,* Dr. Hertzler called pneumonia "the friend of the aged who have been forgotten by their fellows and their God," and now medicine has robbed the old men of that birthright by the use of antibiotics.

We have learned how to keep old men alive, but have uncovered no reason for so doing. *Sans* friends who care, *sans* teeth, often *sans* sight and hearing, and sometimes *sans* the ability to either hold or void his urine, they have nothing to look forward to except one more dreary day.

We have made him artificial teeth, removed his cataracts,

given him hearing aids, and whittled his prostate, but for him there is nothing but bare walls. No kind words to hear, nothing to see that will bring a flicker of interest into his eyes. More comfortable without his artificial dentures, he lies there driveling, while we crow about the wonders of science in prolonging the life of the aged.

He is, indeed, a child again—childlike if not childish—and he has a sore and troublesome spot right where it was in the beginning, and there are no loving arms waiting to comfort him except those of the black angel.

"Better is the end of a thing than the beginning thereof," said Solomon. Death has its compensations for many persons.

Man has performed many roles, some noble and worthy of his Creator, but more of them sinful, worldly, and therefore more entertaining. Instead of life everlasting among the prudes of heaven, maybe he prefers to spend eternity with the fun folk in hell.

Whatever his choice, our prayer for him is that, though everything else be taken from him in his old age, he may, while still remembering the cues he missed and the lines he bungled, be able to laugh at himself until the final curtain falls.

30

Post mortem thoughts

We have only the shell here; the nut is gone.
A EULOGY

Well, Pop, you did your best in your allotted time to be a good husband and father, as well as a responsible citizen of your community. Let us hope that you also did your utmost to foster good feeling in your circle of family and friends, even if you made no great impression on the world in general.

Will the circumstances of your passing cause your associates and relatives to draw closer because of your loss, or will it be a signal for them to fly at one another's throats, like so many wildcats?

One of the last important things you should do on earth is to arrange your affairs so there will be no need of lawsuits or recriminations when the estate comes up for settlement.

For no matter how well you raised your brood, or how congenial your in-laws are, if you die without written instructions as to the disposition of a broken-down wheelbarrow or a battered sofa, they will have the effect of a bone thrown to

Remember that there are distant relatives who may prove grasping.

a bunch of ravenous and savage dogs. "We've been robbed," some of your survivors will say, and they will forever hate those who got the relics.

I am no authority on wills, but I advise you to consult someone who is, and not leave a curse upon your heirs.

If one of your children is unable to look out for himself because of physical or mental handicaps, you should, of course, provide for him as best you can. Otherwise you should leave everything to the surviving partner and allow her to do as she pleases with the money and chattels.

You may be sure she will squander it all on worthless enterprises and fancy clothes, because she has had little training in the business side of your partnership. If you lived with her all those years without preparing her for the job of living within her means, it's your fault, and she has the right to curse you to her last breath.

She may have insisted that you arrange everything beforehand, but that is not the way to handle any kind of business, since conditions change and what is good today may be painfully outdated ten years from now.

Once your children are grown and established in their work you don't owe them a thin dime, but you do owe all to the one who helped you make and save it; and if she decides to blow it all in one year of high living and then go on relief, it's her prerogative.

As long as you are alive and are legally sane, it is a partnership; but when one of you dies, it becomes an individual enterprise, and that's the way you should plan it.

Don't overlook details. I have known men who thought that because they had the property and accounts in joint ownership with right of survivorship, their wives would have no trouble with probate and attorneys; and most of them forgot to indicate joint ownership of the family automobile, which meant the surviving wife either had to burn the thing up or wait months while the courts took their time in settling the question of the rightful owner.

Queer situations come up in this inheritance business, and here you need legal advice as never before. I knew one canny old doctor who kept all his property in his wife's name so that he could beat any malpractice suits that might arise. When his wife died without a will the courts allowed him only a third of the property, giving the balance to his children, who then made him pay rent for his own house. Later they forced him to sell it when they needed the equity for their own projects. Kicked out of the home which he had purchased with his days and nights of hard labor! Robbed of his savings by a bunch of thankless offspring!

Your children, of course, would never do such a thing, but don't forget that their husbands or wives might force them to do so or else cause trouble. Not everyone in this world is strictly honorable and fair, as you have already found out.

I know another case involving two daughters-in-law who, on returning from the cemetery, tore up the old rag rug on the kitchen floor and split it down the middle so the other would get no more than her share, even though it was good for nothing except as a bed for a dog.

If, because of loneliness or poor living conditions, you decide to marry some widow who can cook mush to suit you, the children may try to have you thrown into a mental institution, or at least have you declared incompetent to handle your own affairs, because they feel they have a proprietary interest in the savings of any surviving parent.

This does not apply to my family, and you are sure it is not the case with yours; but human nature being what it is, we should all make our decisions early, inform everyone who might be interested in them, and then have them drawn up in legal form. Remember that there are distant relatives who may prove grasping, so it is best to have things down in black and white and in a form that the courts cannot break too easily.

The briefer and plainer the language, the better the will. Ours was written by the best attorney I could find in Salt Lake City, and there isn't a whereas or a wherefore in it, nor are there any parties of the third or fourth part.

Make a will that fits your own situation, and do it today. Don't get yourself into the mess in which I have found some of my patients. When two of my old patients were preparing for the greatest adventure since their birth, and I was trying to make their passing as comfortable as possible, their children would gang up on me and insist that I withhold drugs that would ease their pain so they could regain consciousness long enough to make their last mark on some deed or grant to the greedy survivors.

One of the great joys of my life is the knowledge that some of these bastards still hate me.

After you make your will, resume living. There are pleasant paths ahead, and as you stroll down them, Grandpa, just remember that you're only old once.